## Elizabeth fac

'I have to thank yo

Perry looked at the _____, ___ ___ ___ ___ of defiance in her eyes. She had not forgiven him for his interference.

'Don't thank me,' he said deliberately. 'My concern was for your father, not yourself. At this present time he has enough to worry him.'

She flushed at that. 'How dare you criticise me? You know nothing of the matter.'

After living in southern Spain for many years, **Meg Alexander** now lives in Kent, although, having been born in Lancashire, she feels that her roots are in the north of England. Meg's career has encompassed a wide variety of roles, from professional cook to assistant director of a conference centre. She has always been a voracious reader, and loves to write. Other loves include history, cats, gardening, cooking and travel. She has a son and two grandchildren.

**Recent titles by the same author:**

THE LOVE CHILD
MIRANDA'S MASQUERADE
HIS LORDSHIP'S DILEMMA
FAREWELL THE HEART

# THE MERRY GENTLEMAN

Meg Alexander

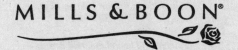

MILLS & BOON®

*First published in Great Britain 1998*
*Harlequin Mills & Boon Limited,*
*Eton House, 18-24 Paradise Road, Richmond, Surrey TW9 1SR*

© Meg Alexander 1998

ISBN 0 263 80801 7

*Set in Times Roman 10½ on 12 pt.*
*04-9806-70894 C1*

*Printed and bound in Great Britain*
*by Caledonian International Book Manufacturing Ltd, Glasgow*

# Chapter One

1794

'Well, I'll be damned!' Lieutenant Peregrine Wentworth stopped abruptly, peering through the darkness at the first floor of the house across the street.

'Probably, old chap, but why just now? What's up?' His companion swayed a little, shaking his head as if to clear it.

'Quiet! Look up there! Don't you see? There's some fellow climbing up that tree. He's almost reached the balcony...'

'Can't see a thing myself through all that greenery. Shouldn't have ordered that last bottle... Sure you ain't mistaken?'

'He's there all right,' Perry whispered. 'Burglary, I shouldn't wonder.'

A branch creaked as the climber tried to conceal himself among the foliage. Perry's deep voice had carried clearly through the still air of the Mediterranean night, and the climber knew himself to have been discovered by the watchers on the ground.

'Blest if you ain't right. Must we fetch him down?'

'Most certainly.' Perry strode to the foot of the tree. 'You, up there, come down at once!'

There was silence from above his head.

'Make haste, or you'll regret it.' Perry gripped his sword, but his words brought no response.

'Very well then, have it your way.' He didn't remove the weapon from its scabbard, but he used it to jab upwards none too gently into the tangled branches.

There was a yelp of anguish and an ominous creaking as the climber tried to scramble higher. Leaves rained down on Perry's head, followed by a shower of twigs. Then the silence returned.

'Stubborn devil, ain't he? Must we shake the tree?'

Perry shook his head. 'If he falls, he'll break his neck. I'll go up after him, Chris.'

'The tree won't bear your weight, old chap...not with him as well. You ain't exactly a midget.'

Perry laughed at this reference to his massive frame. 'It's solid enough at the base. I won't go far. Perhaps I can grab his foot. Here, take this!' He handed his sword to his companion and took a firm grip on the nearest branch.

As he swung himself upwards, he realised that Chris was right. The tree began to sway alarmingly. He reached up a long arm and gave a grunt of satisfaction as his hand came into contact with a booted foot.

'I have you now,' he announced. 'Might as well give it up.'

A volley of imprecations answered him.

'I don't understand a word of this Italian lingo,' Perry replied cheerfully. 'You may as well save your curses for the magistrate.'

'As you may yourself,' said an arctic voice from further along the balcony. 'Take yourself off at once, or I shall summon the Watch.'

Perry was so astonished to hear himself addressed in a cultivated English voice that he almost lost his grip upon the branch. His captive shouted in alarm and began to thrash about.

'Stop that!' Perry shouted. 'You'll send us both headlong...'

The girl on the balcony ran towards them. 'Grip the balustrade, Cesare,' she cried. 'As for you, sir, it would serve you right if your brains were dashed out in the street. For heaven's sake, be quiet! Are you trying to rouse the neighbourhood?'

Perry looked up to see a pale face peering down at him. The balcony and the room behind it were in darkness, so it was impossible to distinguish the girl's features, but he guessed that she was very young.

'I was attempting to do you a service,' he said with dignity. 'I thought this fellow was a burglar.'

'Well, he isn't,' she snapped. 'How dare you refer to Cesare as a "fellow"? He is my...er...my friend, and at least he is no busybody. Go away!'

With that she rapped Perry smartly over the head with what he guessed to be a fan. He reached up to defend himself, and felt the thin struts snap beneath his fingers.

'You...you vandal! Now see what you have done!' The girl reached out to strike at him again, and he dodged aside as a heavy plant pot hurtled towards him, missing his head by inches. It fell to the ground with a resounding crash.

'Charming!' Perry announced. 'You have some curious customs in this country, ma'am. My own friends knock at the front door.'

'Have you any?' she enquired. 'I am surprised to hear it. Haven't you done enough harm for one night?'

The injustice of this accusation left him speechless. Boiling with indignation, he began to lower himself to the ground.

There he found Chris convulsed with silent laughter.

'It wasn't funny!' Perry said in an injured tone. 'She might have stunned me with that plant pot.'

This sent Chris into fresh whoops of glee. 'I guessed she wasn't pleased,' he gasped. 'Tell you what, old chap, you've disturbed a lovers' tryst.'

'How was I to know? The damned fellow didn't have a guitar.'

This finished Chris completely. For some moments he was unable to speak. When he did, it was to assure his friend that to serenade a lady was more usual in Spain.

'That's by the way,' Perry said darkly. 'A lovers' tryst? Why, that little hellcat is just a child! Couldn't see her face too well, but she can't be above fifteen. What a temper! She'd benefit from a sound beating.'

'It's the Latin temperament,' Chris said wisely. 'These Italians are a hot-blooded lot.'

'But she wasn't Italian. Her English is as good as

yours or mine. No trace of an accent. I'd stake my life that she is one of us.'

'Well, it ain't much of a mystery. Italy was always popular with our countrymen who made the Grand Tour. Now, old chap, the night is young. What do you say to sharing another bottle before we go back to the ship?'

'That's the best idea you've had all evening. I could use a glass of wine after that experience.' He began to chuckle. 'It has taught me a lesson,' he admitted. 'From now on, these Italian fellows may shin up trees and walls without another word from me.'

The humour of the situation struck him suddenly and he too began to laugh. In great good humour they strolled together to the far end of the street, kicking aside the broken plant pot as they went.

Perry glanced about him. 'This place is like the tomb. I thought the commotion must have brought someone into the street. And not a tavern in sight.'

At the end of the street they found themselves in a deserted square, lit only by a single beam of light from a window not yet shuttered against the evening air.

'Nothing here.' Chris looked about him in disgust. 'We must be in the wealthier part of the city, though you'd never guess it with all these blank walls.'

'I hear they keep their treasures hidden inside. Possibly they ain't too fond of noise.'

'Well, they don't mind smells, apparently. God, there's a stench! It's worse than London. Just look at the gutters! They are heaving!'

'Only a rat or two. Let's go back. We're bound

to find something better than those drink shops round the docks.'

'Very well. A good stiff brandy wouldn't come amiss.' Chris turned and began to retrace his steps, but Perry had stopped beside what looked like a discarded bundle of clothing.

'Hang on!' he said. 'I thought I heard a moan.'

Chris pushed at the bundle with his foot. 'Just some poor devil sleeping rough,' he said. 'I tell you, Perry, I never saw so many beggars in my life as here in Genoa.' He heard the tinkle of coins as Perry bent down.

'At it again?' he chaffed. 'I hope his friends ain't lurking close. At the sound of money they'll be down on us like a pack of wolves.'

Perry grinned at him. 'They won't attack two English officers. They must know we are armed.'

'Even so, it ain't a bad idea to get away from here. Come on, after eight weeks living on salt beef I've a thirst that will take some quenching.'

'You've done your best this evening,' Perry teased him. 'You won't tell me that you ain't just a trifle bosky?'

'Not a bit of it. It will take more than this Italian wine to put me on my back.'

'Boasting again? Admit it, you were somewhat up in the world an hour ago. I thought...' Whatever he was about to say was lost as they heard another moan. A few quick steps took Perry back to the figure on the ground.

'Are you hurt?' he asked. Then he looked up in exasperation. 'Damme, he can't understand me.'

'Yes, I do,' a faint voice murmured. 'Will you help me? I've been attacked.'

'Are you English, sir?' Perry fell to his knees beside the man.

'Yes. If you could raise me to my feet...? I took a blow to the head which rendered me unconscious.'

'You need water,' Perry said decisively. He bent and raised the victim in his arms. A few long strides took him to the fountain in the middle of the square. There he soaked his handkerchief and wiped at the bloody face of what was clearly an elderly man.

'You need more light,' Chris said quietly. 'Bring him over here to where the lamp is shining from that window.'

There, both men could see that the wound was still pouring blood.

'You need a doctor, sir. Do you know of anyone close by?'

'Just take me home,' the old man pleaded. 'My house is just around the corner. I'll send my man to fetch the surgeon.'

'Can you walk if we assist you?'

'I'll try.' The man struggled to his feet and then sank back again. 'I'm sorry, but I feel so faint.'

'If you will allow me, sir.' Perry picked up the thin figure with ease, marvelling that a grown man could feel so light and fragile. 'Will you give me your direction?'

'Over there, in the street on the left...the Villa Castiglione...' The weak voice died away.

'He's fainted again, but it shouldn't take long to find it.' Perry began to follow the directions, untroubled by the slight weight of his burden. 'Can you make out the names?'

'This must be the place. Wait a moment, Perry! Ain't this the house where we saw the burglar?

There's the tree, and the plant pot scattered about the ground.'

'No matter. Knock them up! The old man's losing a lot of blood.'

Chris beat a tattoo upon the massive wooden doors. Then they swung open and an astonished porter barred their way.

'Stand aside!' Perry ordered briefly. 'Your master has been injured. Bestir yourself! He needs a doctor.'

He looked up to find himself under scrutiny by a major-domo. This individual wasted no time on questioning. A quick word dispatched a footman on the necessary errand and he led the way up a curving staircase.

'This is Mr Grantham's room.' He threw open a door upon the first floor. 'What can I do to help?'

'We need water to wash the blood away, and cloths to staunch the flow, smelling salts, and perhaps brandy... Oh, better not the latter for a head wound. If we get him into bed, he'll be more comfortable.'

The major-domo gave his orders quickly. Then he looked at Perry. 'If you'll excuse me, sir, Miss Elizabeth must be told.'

'Not just yet, I think. A screaming woman is all we need.'

'Miss Elizabeth will not scream, sir.'

'Very well. You must do as you think best. Meantime, you might hand me a clean nightshirt.'

'I will send for Mr Grantham's valet, sir.'

It was unfortunate that Miss Elizabeth Grantham arrived before the valet. Barefoot, with her hair in disarray, and clad only in her night attire, she was exposed to the full horror of the situation.

She did not flinch at the sight which met her eyes, though the floor of her father's bedchamber was scattered with bloodstained clothing. A sharp intake of breath was the only sign of her distress. Then she hurried across the room to bend over the prone figure on the bed.

'Father?'

'He can't hear you, ma'am. He is still unconscious.'

'How bad is it?'

'I believe it is but a flesh wound, but we have sent for the surgeon.' Perry had recognised her at once.

This was the girl he had seen previously on the balcony. He knew it before she spoke, but when she did so the clear, autocratic voice was unmistakable.

She turned and looked at him. Then her eyes widened.

'You?' she said in disbelief.

Perry bowed. 'First Lieutenant Peregrine Wentworth, of HMS *Artemis*, ma'am. This is Lord Christopher Rainham.'

The introduction did not faze her in the least. She nodded briefly, and turned to take her father's hand. His wound was still bleeding freely, soaking the compress on his brow, and his pallor was alarming.

Elizabeth felt about her blindly for something to staunch the flow, and Perry thrust a cloth into her hand. Then he saw that she was shaking.

'Let me!' he said. 'Pray don't distress yourself, Miss Grantham. Head wounds bleed profusely. The blow must have been severe, but it may not be as serious as you fear.'

'He...he looks ghastly.' Her voice was not quite under control.

'That may be due to shock, rather than a fatal injury. The surgeon will tell us more.'

She turned to face him then, her face drained of all colour, and Perry caught his breath. Even in her distress, she was quite the most beautiful woman he had ever seen. In the light of the candles her dark hair gleamed like a raven's wing, but it was her eyes which held him. Huge and lustrous, they were almost black.

Though she was very young, she was not the child he had at first supposed. He guessed her to be seventeen or so, but she seemed to be mature beyond her years. There was strength of character in that determined little chin, and a certain promise in the wilful, mobile mouth.

Beside him, he heard Christopher gasp. Then his lordship advanced towards Elizabeth.

'Will you not take a little brandy, ma'am?' he suggested gently. 'You too have suffered a shock.'

Elizabeth straightened her back. Then her chin went up. 'It won't be necessary. I shall not faint.' She rose and faced the two men. 'I should like to know what happened, if you please?'

'We were walking through the square—' Perry had no opportunity to say more. It was at this moment that the surgeon bustled into the room. Ignoring Elizabeth's protests, he demanded to be left alone with his patient, and she had no alternative but to obey him.

As she preceded the two young men down the

massive staircase, her stiff carriage warned Perry of her displeasure. He smiled to himself. This young lady was unaccustomed to having her wishes thwarted. He was forced to accord her a certain amount of grudging admiration. She had neither screamed nor fainted at the shocking sight which met her eyes. A cool creature, this, with a will of iron. He could only guess what it had cost her to maintain her self-control.

Admirable, of course, but her faults outweighed her virtues. Personally, he had no taste for hellcats, beautiful though she was.

She stalked across the marble hall ahead of them and led them into an ornate salon. Motioning to them to take a seat, she then rang for refreshments.

Chris was quick to protest. 'Really, ma'am, there is no need to trouble yourself. You cannot wish for company at this time.'

'I wish to hear what happened.' Pale, but composed, she seated herself opposite.

'As I told you, Miss Grantham, we were walking through the square when we heard your father call for help. He must have been attacked, though we saw no one in the vicinity. He was able to tell us where he lived, so we brought him here.' Perry made his explanation as brief as possible.

'Then I must thank you, gentlemen.' She offered each of them a glass of wine, though she did not touch her own. 'Possibly you have saved his life. We are in your debt.'

Perry gave her a curious look. She was the oddest creature. So tiny that her feet barely touched the ground as she sat in the wing chair, she now reminded him of a child playing at being a hostess. A glance at her face swiftly disabused him of that idea. The martial light in her eyes made him suspect that she had guessed his thoughts.

'So!' she said coolly. 'You are officers in the British Navy?'

'Yes, ma'am, put into Genoa for watering and provisions.'

The information did not appear to interest her. After satisfying herself that their glasses were empty, she rose.

'I thank you again for your timely intervention.' Elizabeth held out her hand. 'You will excuse me if I don't offer you further hospitality, but under the circumstances...'

'Quite understandable, ma'am.' Chris accepted his dismissal with good grace, but Perry was incensed. His bow was stiff in the extreme.

It was not until they reached the street that he spoke again. 'That woman should have been drowned at birth,' he announced with feeling. 'She ain't even human.'

'Oh, come on, Perry, you can't blame her for not wanting to do the pretty. She had a shock, you know, and she must be worried sick about her father. Besides, she's little more than a child—'

'But old enough to have a lover. It ain't at all the thing to have men climbing through her bedroom window.'

'Turned prudish, have you?' Chris began to chuckle. 'Admit it, you ain't forgiven her for that flowerpot.'

'She may do as she pleases,' Perry said stiffly.

'Though I think she might have allowed us to wait for the surgeon's verdict.'

'Nothing to do with us, old chap. Best forget it. I say, though, she is a beauty, isn't she? Those eyes could make men weaken at the knees.'

'You've been at sea too long. She looks well enough, I suppose, but she don't appeal to me. Imagine living with that tongue! A spoiled brat, too self-assured by half, and arrogant with it.'

'Would you have liked her better if she'd fainted at the sight of blood?' The question was innocent enough, but Chris's eyes were twinkling.

'I don't like her at all.'

'Hmm! She certainly made an impression on you.'

'That she did, and all of it unfavourable.'

'You are growing sour in your old age. Didn't you look about you, Perry? I shouldn't be surprised if she ain't an heiress. The treasures in the hall alone are worth a fortune.'

'Then I wish good luck to the man who takes her on. He'd need to be stone-deaf.'

Chris began to laugh, and after a moment Perry joined him. 'Sorry!' he said. 'I'm behaving like a bear with a sore head.'

'Might have been worse if she hadn't missed you with the pot.'

Perry grinned. 'I never met a woman yet who could hit a barn door at ten paces.'

'Thank the Lord for that! Now, ain't that a tavern that I see before me...the handle towards my hand?'

'Culture, too?' Perry aimed a playful blow at his friend. 'Don't parody *Macbeth*, old son. It's more than I can stand at present. Let's sample some low life, for a change.'

They pushed their way into the crowded inn. It was only when they were seated at a table in the corner that Perry noticed the parlous state of his uniform.

'Devil take it!' he announced. 'I might have been in a slaughterhouse.'

The condition of his garments bore this out. His previously immaculate whites now bore clear evidence of bloodstains. They were also muddied at the knees where he had knelt down by the fountain.

Well aware of the curious glances of the other customers, he made an unsuccessful attempt to draw his blue coat together across his massive chest.

'Won't do to let the captain see you in that state,' Chris murmured. 'Bad for the image of the British Navy. We'd best get back to the ship.'

'Not before we've finished this bottle. No one will see us when we go aboard. I'll slip down to my cabin.'

'Hope you manage it, otherwise you'll be in for an unpleasant interview tomorrow.'

Thankfully, this dire prediction went unfulfilled, and their return to the *Artemis* went unremarked by their redoubtable captain.

For the next three days his duties aboard kept Perry fully occupied. Absorbed with the problems of repairs, provisioning, and certain matters of discipline, the night's adventures faded from his mind.

It was therefore with some surprise that he opened an invitation for himself and Chris to dine with Mr Grantham on the following day.

'The old man must be feeling better. Now you can set your mind at rest about him.'

'You can!' Perry said with meaning. 'I've no wish to go in order to cross swords with that wench again.'

'Sorry, old chap, I can't oblige you. I'm on duty.'

'I could claim to be on duty too.' Perry smoothed the note between his fingers.

'Too churlish, Perry. Why not spare him an hour or two? Besides, I thought you planned to go ashore. Don't you have commissions for your family? You mentioned tobacco, and a pipe or two of wine...'

'I could get them at Gibraltar.'

Chris shook his head. 'You won't get Italian wine there. Didn't you tell me that Barolo was your mother's favourite?'

'That's true, always supposing that the custom officers won't be difficult when we dock at Portsmouth.'

'It's worth a try. Give my regards to the siren of the balcony.' He dodged aside as Perry advanced towards him. 'No, no! You can't fight me! I am the shorter by four inches, and you give me at least three stones in weight.'

'Wretch!' As Perry threw a cushion at Chris's head, he was laughing.

However, it was in no easy frame of mind that he stepped into the bum-boat on the following day, resplendent in full dress uniform.

His commissions were soon accomplished, but he was strangely reluctant to return to the Villa Castiglione. For a time he wandered about the narrow streets of Genoa, and it was growing dusk before he forced himself to make his way to the wealthy quarter of the city. As he lifted the knocker on the heavy door, he vowed to take his leave of Mr Grantham as soon as politeness would allow.

To his relief the old man was alone. Apart from a bandage round his head, he showed no other signs of injury.

One bright eye inspected Perry as he walked into the room.

'How are you feeling now, sir?' Perry shook the proffered hand.

'Much better, Mr Wentworth, though the surgeon tells me I was lucky not to lose an eye. My dear sir, I owe my life to you. Words are not sufficient to express my gratitude.'

'You would have done the same for me, I believe. It was fortunate that we happened by. Lord Christopher sends his apologies, sir. His duties made it impossible for him to accept your kind invitation.'

Mr Grantham nodded. 'You young men are fully occupied these days. Tell me, what do you think of the present situation in France? I won't deny that it concerns me.'

'I am no politician, sir. Here in Genoa, you are safe enough from the fervour of the revolutionary movement.'

'Are we, Mr Wentworth? I do not share your hopes. That French mob? Fanatics, to a man! Will they stay within their borders? Not a hope of it, in my opinion.'

'Mr Grantham, they are ill-disciplined...ill-led... Against the armies of the Allies they would stand no chance.'

'Possibly not, but they may not see it in that light.

Since they executed the Queen and their King they
are drunk with power...'

Perry was silent. There seemed little he could say.

'Poor lady!' Mr Grantham sighed. 'Whatever her
mistakes, she did not deserve that fate. Now bloodlust sweeps the country. They have set up guillotines
in every town...'

Mr Grantham was growing agitated, and Perry felt
moved to intervene.

'My dear sir, don't distress yourself. This is a
matter for the French alone.'

His host smiled faintly. 'I see you are no politician, Mr Wentworth. There is a new spirit abroad in
Europe. These revolutionaries, with their talk of lib-
erty, brotherhood and equality, intend to take their
message further. Even if they did not, they must
consider the enemy at their gates.'

'You speak of Britain and her allies?'

'Indeed, my boy. If the French should decide to
strike first, they will sweep through this part of Italy
down to Naples.'

'You may be right,' Perry said slowly. 'Captain
Nelson in the *Ariadne* was ordered to make all haste
to the Court there, to see how matters stand with the
King.'

'It bears out my worst fears.' The old man's eyes
were sad. 'I must think of my family.'

'Sir, could you not take ship for England?'

'Would that I could, but my wife is in poor health.
She could not stand the journey. You will excuse
her if she leaves us after we have dined? It has been
something of an effort for her to appear this evening,
but she was determined to meet you for herself.'

Perry bowed. '*Madame* should not have troubled

herself. Indeed, sir, there was not the least need for you to feel obliged to entertain me.'

'There I must beg to differ. Now, here is Elizabeth, come to welcome you...'

Perry rose to his feet. Gowned simply in white, with a knot of azure ribbons at her breast, Elizabeth had no need of further embellishment for her charms. In spite of his dislike of her, he was forced to admit that she was indeed a beauty. Dark, silky curls, cut *à la* Sappho, framed the little heart-shaped face and emphasised the brilliance of her enormous eyes.

Now those eyes were wary, though she was smiling with perfect civility as she greeted him. Perry was reminded of his nephews, summoned to account for some misdeed, as Elizabeth shot a searching glance at her father's face.

Perry's lips twitched in amusement. She is wondering if I have betrayed her, he thought to himself. His countenance was grave as he took her hand, but she had seen the smile, and resented it. A second glance at her father appeared to reassure her, and the wary look was replaced by one of crushing dignity.

Mr Grantham reached out an arm to draw her to his side. 'Have you lost your tongue, my love?' he teased. 'If so, it will be for the first time.'

'Of course not, Father. Excuse me!' A delicate flush of colour touched her cheeks. 'Welcome to our home, Mr Wentworth.'

Perry sensed that she was struggling for composure. The memory of that scene upon the balcony was clearly uppermost in her mind, and she would not meet his eyes.

'Your stepmother is come down, dearest?' Mr Grantham struggled to his feet.

Elizabeth nodded.

'Then come! We must not keep her waiting.' He reached for his stick and followed his daughter and their guest as Elizabeth led the way across the hall. He was limping heavily, and for the first time Perry realised that his host was badly crippled.

'Sir, you were more badly injured than I had supposed. Will you not take my arm?'

'No need for that, my boy. This game leg is the result of an old riding accident. I have learned to cope with it.' He urged Perry into the salon and towards the lady lying on a sofa by the fire.

'Lucia, my dear, this is Mr Wentworth. I know you wish to thank him for his services to me.'

'I do, indeed.' Smiling, Lucia Grantham held out her hand. 'My dear sir, what am I to say to you? Without your help my husband might have died. Will you accept my deepest gratitude?'

Perry took the frail hand and kissed it. Beside this tiny creature he felt larger than ever, and as clumsy as an ox. She seemed to sense his feelings, and patted the seat beside her. In her prettily accented English she began to draw him out, asking about his family in England.

'You must miss them sadly,' she went on. 'I hear that you have been at sea these many months.'

'Yes, ma'am, but I hope to see them shortly. We shall soon be on our way to Portsmouth.'

'I have never been to England, but when my health improves....'

'Mama, that may be sooner than you think.'

Elizabeth's tone was encouraging. 'You know you have been feeling stronger in these past few weeks.'

Husband and wife exchanged a glance, and Perry felt a pang of pity. Lucia Grantham was clearly very ill. Traces of beauty were still apparent in her ravaged features, but her skin bore a yellowish tinge. In the gaunt face her eyes were sunken and shadowed with pain.

His fears were confirmed when she was wheeled into the dining-room in a bathchair, but though she barely touched the food her spirit was indomitable. At a sign from her, Elizabeth rose when the meal had ended.

'Will you excuse me, Mr Wentworth? I must obey my doctor. He insists that I must rest.' The sick woman gave him a rueful smile, but it was clear that the effort to speak was becoming too much for her.

Perry took her hand and raised it to his lips. 'I appreciate your kindness to me, ma'am. May I offer my sincere wishes for your speedy recovery?'

She nodded, and signalled to Elizabeth to wheel her from the room.

Perry looked at his host. 'Sir, I feel that I should leave you now. I've trespassed upon your hospitality for too long.'

'Don't go, I beg of you, Mr Wentworth. Won't you sit down? I have something to discuss with you.'

# Chapter Two

Perry was at a loss to understand the anxiety in Mr Grantham's tone. For a moment he wondered if news of Elizabeth's escapade had reached her father's ears.

His host was silent for some time, but when he spoke at last it was upon another subject.

'Doubtless you believe that my fears are groundless,' the old man said in a low voice. 'But let me ask you something. Have you ever lived in an occupied country where you were the enemy?'

Perry shook his head.

'I have. It is not a fate that I could wish upon my daughter.'

'My dear sir, Italy is not occupied—'

'It will come. I am convinced of it, as I explained to you. As you see, I cannot travel with Lucia in her present state of health, but I have been wondering…will your captain allow Elizabeth to take passage on your ship? She has relatives in England.'

Perry was astounded. 'Mr Grantham, it would be impossible,' he protested. 'The *Artemis* is a warship.

On the passage home we are more than likely to be attacked. Your daughter will be safer here with you.'

'No! I must get her away. Three days ago I was reminded of my own mortality—what will happen to her when I am no longer here? Lucia cannot care for her.'

'Then why not arrange a passage for her on a merchant vessel? There are many such in the docks at present.'

'All of them unarmed. Can you tell me that they won't be attacked?'

'No, sir, but it is your only hope. Captain Robsart will take no passengers on the *Artemis*.'

'Mr Wentworth, will you ask him? He would not lose by it. If it is a question of money...?'

'That would not weigh with him,' Perry said stiffly. 'It is a matter of navy rules and regulations.'

'I see that I have offended you. Forgive me...I feel quite distracted.' The lines on the old face deepened. 'I don't know what to do.'

'Mr Grantham, let me beg you to consider. Even were it possible, you can have no idea of the sheer discomfort on a warship. Your daughter has been gently bred...'

This brought a smile to the face of his host. 'Don't be deceived by her appearance, sir. Elizabeth is tougher than you might at first suppose.'

Perry needed no convincing, but he would not be put off. 'Mr Grantham, you have had a shock,' he said doggedly. 'When you are recovered, you will see the folly...excuse me, I mean...the undesirability of what you are suggesting.'

'I shall not change my mind.' The lines about the old man's mouth had hardened. 'Elizabeth was a late

joy. Her mother died when she was born. All I have
left of her to remind me is this child of my heart.
Naturally, I love Lucia, but blood calls to blood. Mr
Wentworth, I am asking for your help. Will you not
save my daughter? At least, speak to your captain.'

'I'll try, sir, but I cannot offer much hope.' Perry
was powerless to resist the impassioned appeal. 'Mr
Grantham, I must thank you once again for a very
pleasant evening.' He rose to take his leave. As Mrs
Grantham had retired, he would not be required to
join the ladies in the salon, and he was glad of it.
He had reckoned without his host.

'Elizabeth will be waiting for us,' Mr Grantham
murmured.

Perry resigned himself to a further exchange of
courtesies, but it was soon borne in upon him that
he had misjudged the daughter of the house.

A raised eyebrow from his host and a quick nod
from Elizabeth sent Mr Grantham up to bid his wife
goodnight. Then his companion wasted no time. She
faced him squarely.

'I have to thank you, sir. You did not betray me.'

Perry looked at the lifted chin, and saw the flash
of defiance in her eyes. She had not forgiven him
for his interference.

'Don't thank me,' he said deliberately. 'My concern was for your father, not yourself. At this present
time he has enough to worry him.'

She flushed at that. 'How dare you criticise me?
You know nothing of the matter.'

'Enough to know that you have no business adding to his worries.'

'Ha!' she said. 'I knew from the moment I first

saw you…bombastic, priggish, arrogant and insufferable!'

'Leave out the priggish, and we might be twins,' he suggested sweetly.

'Why, you worm! Who are you to criticise my conduct?'

'At least I don't throw pots.'

'Oh, did you think I threw it?' She dimpled delightfully. 'That is famous! I wish I had, but I didn't think of it. I caught it with my elbow. You may be sure that if I'd aimed, I should not have missed.'

'A charming accomplishment! Have you any others?'

'Oh, yes!' she assured him in an airy tone. 'I have learned to damp pretension—'

'What!' he shouted.

'A sore point, sir? Believe me, you may swagger about the streets of Genoa with your cronies, dressed to the nines, and expecting the world to grovel at your feet, but I am not so easily taken in.'

'Of course not!' he snarled. 'With years of experience behind you, you would be a match for any mushroom squire.'

This reference to her tender years caused Elizabeth to bridle. 'It does not take a lifetime of experience to know a busybody, sir.'

'Naturally not, especially when one's preference lies with some monkey who scrambles in the branches of a tree.'

'You cannot be referring to Count Cesare di Tavola. His family history goes back five hundred years.'

'Without learning the use of a door?'

Elizabeth eyed him with acute dislike. 'I shall not

trouble to answer that remark,' she replied in icy tones. 'One cannot, after all, cast pearls before swine.'

'One can, however, point out the impropriety of receiving a gentleman in one's chamber, clad only in a night-robe.'

Hot colour flooded Elizabeth's face. 'How dare you?' she cried. 'I did not receive him. I didn't even know that he was there until he threw the pebble at my window—' She stopped, furious with herself for attempting to justify her behaviour.

'You should have thrown it back,' Perry said tersely.

'Moralising, sir? I don't expect it from a sailor, of all people. I have yet to discover how any of my actions can possibly concern you.' There was a dangerous glitter in her eyes.

'They don't...not in the least.'

'Then pray keep your sermons for those who wish to hear them. You, I must suppose, are a model of all the virtues...'

'No, I ain't.' Perry shook his head, anxious to refute this outrageous statement. He was aware suddenly that his behaviour as a guest left much to be desired. 'The truth is that I'm often in hot water, so I know what it's like to be hauled over the coals. I beg your pardon.'

Elizabeth stared at him. Then, somewhat mollified by this confession, she decided to accept the olive branch.

'I shall ring for the tea-tray,' she announced with dignity.

'You keep up with the English custom, then? I had not thought to find it here in Genoa.'

'We are not barbarians,' she told him coldly. 'Mrs Benson tells me that to take tea in the evening after dinner is quite the latest thing.'

'Mrs Benson? She is your governess?'

Elizabeth's eyes flashed. 'My governess? Sir, I am not a child. In March I shall be seventeen—' Her hand flew to her mouth. 'Oh, I had forgot…a lady does not mention her age, but you provoked me into doing so.' She tried to hide her confusion.

Perry hid a smile. 'My apologies, ma'am. I had not thought you so close to decrepitude.'

She gave him a dagger-look. 'Laugh if you will, but I am out in society. In fact, I am betrothed. Count Cesare has offered for me.'

'And your father has agreed?' Perry was incredulous and it showed. If it were true, Mr Grantham would not have suggested sending Elizabeth to England.

Under his keen scrutiny, she looked uncomfortable.

'Well, not exactly, but he will…he must… Papa thinks Cesare unsuitable, but that is because he does not know him well. When they grow to understand each other better…' Her voice trailed away.

Wisely, Perry did not offer an opinion, but he was beginning to understand much that had previously been a mystery to him. This, then, was why the Count had found it necessary to attempt a clandestine meeting.

Perry began to wonder about the fellow. If Mr Grantham had taken against him, there must be a good reason. Even on short acquaintance he'd been impressed by the old man's shrewdness. Was the Count a fortune-hunter? It must be so. On the face of it, a marriage with a member of the Italian aristocracy must ensure Elizabeth's safety.

'Well, sir, have you nothing to say?' Elizabeth looked triumphant.

'Ma'am?'

'I mean about my offer,' she cried impatiently.

'Remarkable!' Perry surveyed her with a lifted eyebrow.

For a moment he thought that she would strike him.

'You are quite the most detestable man I ever met,' she told him in a voice which shook with rage. 'But for my father, I should order you from this house at once.'

'Throwing things after me?' He began to laugh. 'You will not wish to break another fan, Miss Grantham, and the vases in this room are more valuable than a flowerpot.'

He thought she would explode with fury. Then the door opened and her father came to join them. Preoccupied with his own thoughts, he seemed unaware of the tense atmosphere in the room.

'Mr Wentworth, how long do you remain in Genoa?' he asked.

'It is impossible to say with certainty, but possibly for another week, sir. Much will depend upon the shipwrights, and the availability of provisions.'

'Then I trust that you will give us the pleasure of your company again. Lord Christopher, too, and also your captain, if he should care to dine with us.'

'You are too generous, Mr Grantham.' Perry did not commit himself. 'Regrettably, Captain Robsart does not often dine ashore.'

He shuddered inwardly, aware of the likely consequences if the captain found himself under pressure to offer passage to Elizabeth.

'Then I shall remind you of your promise to speak to him on my behalf.'

Perry was not proof against the pleading in the old man's eyes. 'I won't forget, but as I told you—'

'Yes, yes, I understand, but you will do your best?'

'I will.' Perry rose to take his leave, with renewed thanks for a pleasant evening. Pleasure was not, perhaps, the sensation uppermost in his mind, but the invitation had been kindly meant. It was a pity that it had included a request from Mr Grantham which could not possibly be granted. Worse had been the need to spend the past few hours in the company of this maddening girl.

'Now, my boy, allow me to ring for the carriage. You will take it to the docks?'

'I shouldn't think of turning your people out at this late hour,' Perry was quick to protest.

'Was not my experience sufficient warning to you not to walk alone at night?'

'I am armed, sir.' Perry tapped his sword significantly.

'And possessed of a Herculean frame?' Mr Grantham smiled up at the tall figure of his guest. 'I must confess that it would be a brave man who tried to mill you down. Shall we say next Sunday, then?'

Perry hesitated, well aware that Elizabeth was willing him to refuse. Some imp of mischief persuaded him to agree, and he saw her stiffen.

'I'll do my best.' He beamed at her. 'Though it must depend upon my duties.'

With that he took his leave, knowing that if looks
could kill, he would have fallen lifeless at
Elizabeth's feet.

As he strode back through the darkened streets,
he pondered on the events of what had proved to be
a strange evening. He'd warmed to the charm of Mr
Grantham and his wife, but the girl?

At least their dislike was mutual, but honesty
compelled him to admit that his own behaviour had
not been beyond reproach. He had criticised her
morals when he had no right to do so. Perhaps his
strictures were unfounded. She'd claimed that the
Count's visit had taken her by surprise, and she
hadn't even thrown the flowerpot—that had been an
accident. Worst of all, he had treated her like a child,
and that had stung her pride.

He began to smile. She was little more, after all,
in spite of her attempts to appear sophisticated. And
when she was at a loss, she blushed quite charmingly. Strange how that rosy colour crept across the
flawless skin, as smooth and creamy as a magnolia
petal.

He frowned, remembering her angry words. That
she was a beauty he would not deny. She was also
wilful, stubborn, opinionated and thoroughly
spoiled.

No other woman of his acquaintance, with the
possible exception of Prudence, his brother's wife,
would have challenged him as Elizabeth had done.
If they ever met, those two ladies would deal fa-
mously together. Both were quick and intelligent,
and neither hesitated to speak her mind.

But at sixteen? Perry shook his head. The Count
was welcome to her. That wild streak would take

some holding. God help the man unwise enough to take her to wife. She was likely to be a handful.

He stopped as a thought struck him. Was he actually prosing like some greybeard? The notion would send his family into whoops. Perry's hasty temper and impulsive nature had led him into many scrapes, and his mother often shook her head over his apparent wildness.

But that was long ago. He was older now. At the advanced age of twenty-four he could look back with a degree of kindly tolerance upon his youthful follies.

This sense of lofty superiority did not survive an interview with Chris.

'Been a-wooing, old chap?' his friend enquired.

The ensuing scuffle was unedifying and ended only when the bosun put his head round the door.

'Gentlemen, please!' he implored. 'Cap'n's wondering where the noise is coming from.'

Perry straightened his coat. 'I have *not* been a-wooing,' he announced darkly when the man had gone. 'Best brace yourself! Mr Grantham hopes to put his daughter aboard for the voyage to England.'

'No! You're gammoning me!'

'It's true. He begs that I will ask the captain.'

'Rather you than me! Perry, he can't mean it. Why would he suggest such a thing?'

'Safety? He believes that the French will invade Italy.'

'That rabble?' Chris's tone was scornful. 'When they tried it in Belgium and Holland they were defeated.'

'I can't persuade him otherwise.'

'Must have been that knock upon the head. You must see that it isn't possible.'

'I see it, but he does not. He means it, and it ain't due to his injury. He's recovering well.'

'And what of the fair siren of the balcony? Does she agree with the idea?'

'She knows nothing of it, thank God! Heaven knows what she might have done.'

'More flying pots, you think?'

Perry smiled at that. 'It was an accident, so she tells me. She dislodged it with her elbow.'

'So you've made your peace with her?'

'Not a hope, old chap!'

'She didn't apologise?'

'She did not. In fact, she told me that if she'd aimed, she wouldn't have missed.'

Chris shouted with laughter. 'A quiet evening, you said? It don't sound like it to me. What happened to your well-known charm? By now, I thought she'd be eating out of your hand.'

'Very amusing! Possibly you'll have more success with her.'

'What do you mean?'

'You are invited to dine at the villa on Sunday.'

'No, no! I won't stand in your way. With me there you won't have a chance.'

'Sadly, I must dash your hopes. She plans to wed that fellow in the tree…claims to be betrothed to him.'

'That mountebank? Yellow to the core. If he'd had anything about him, he'd have given you a facer.'

'He could have tried.' Perry's eyes began to twinkle. 'He's Italian…a count or some such thing.'

'Then it should have been rapiers at dawn. What a hum! It's a pity that we missed it.'

'Save your bloodlust for the French,' Perry advised. 'Now, will you come or not?'

'That depends. Do you mean to speak to Captain Robsart?'

'I gave my word.'

'Then you'd best go now, whilst you are still pot-valiant.'

'It will do tomorrow, wretch! By the way, I am not pot-valiant. It was a sober evening.'

'Can't have been, or you'd never have agreed. I suspect that I'll be going alone to the villa. You'll be below…in chains.'

On the following day it seemed as if this dire prediction was likely to be fulfilled. The kindest remark which Perry received from his superior officer was a request to know if he had quite run mad. His disclaimer brought down a flood of imprecations upon his head. The captain swore for several minutes, during which time he did not repeat himself.

Distinctly shaken, Perry escaped at last to rejoin his shipmates.

'No luck?' Chris asked wickedly.

'You might say that. Just listen! He's still bellowing…'

'He'll get over it. Mr Grantham will be disappointed, though, and so am I. The fair Elizabeth would have livened up the voyage. What will you say to him?'

'I've already warned him that his plan was out of the question. Hopefully, he'll accept it.'

\* \* \*

This hope was soon to be dashed. On the following Sunday, though Mr Grantham met his guest with his usual courtesy, he could not hide his dismay at Perry's news.

Clasping his hands, rocking back and forth in anguish, he appealed to them once more.

'You can't have heard the news from Toulon,' he cried. 'The British are driven out...'

'Mr Grantham, it can't be true! Our people were to hold the town until the arrival of reinforcements.'

'The British government refused to send more troops. Admiral Hood has taken off some fifteen thousand refugees, but the rest... I cannot bear to think of it. Even the guillotines are not enough for the bloodlust of the revolutionaries. Many have been shot down where they stood. Others, including two young English girls, were chained together and thrown into the river.'

'These may be rumours, sir. I can't believe that that ill-led rabble could succeed against our men.'

'Ill-led, Mr Wentworth? Believe me, they have found a leader. The man is a Corsican, a technical expert, though he is little more than a boy. His brilliance at Toulon was such that he is already promoted General of Brigade.'

'That may not signify,' Chris protested. 'They have executed their best generals. Mr Grantham, can you be sure that your news is true?'

'I am certain of it. My informants are well-placed.' He pressed his thin hands to his face as if to shut out terrible visions.

Both young men were deeply shocked by his words, but Perry made an attempt to comfort him.

'Sir, these massacres are terrible, but they took place far away. Pray don't disturb yourself unduly. The French have no quarrel with this country. Here in Italy you must be safe—'

'For how long? I am no soothsayer, but let us suppose that this gifted soldier should decide to make himself master of all Europe? Then there would be no escape.'

'I think you have forgot the British Navy, sir.' Chris spoke up proudly in the defence of his own service.

'No, Lord Christopher, I have not.' A wan smile appeared on the face of his host. 'But even if Britain holds the seas, what of the land? We need another Marlborough.'

Both his companions were silent. In the recent war in North America, leadership of the British Army had left much to be desired. The incompetence of the generals and the bravery of their opponents had led to the colonists gaining independence from the mother country. King George was known to regard it as the greatest disaster of his long reign.

Mr Grantham sighed. 'Do you understand my worries, gentlemen? I assure you that they are not just the feeble wanderings of an old man.'

'Of course not,' Perry assured him quietly. 'But, Mr Grantham, even supposing that you are right, what you ask is impossible. Captain Robsart won't consider it.'

'Very well, then, I won't press you further. Shall we join the ladies?'

Lord Christopher was at his best in feminine company. He seated himself by Mrs Grantham, and soon had her laughing at his tales of London society.

Even Elizabeth lost her wary look and, armed by his evident admiration, she gave him an enchanting smile. Dressed in a simple gown of jonquil yellow caught down the front with tiny pearl buttons to match the seed pearls on the banding of her puffed sleeves, she was looking ravishing.

Perry smiled to himself. His friend seemed to be fatally smitten by the brilliance of her dark eyes, the low, musical voice, and the grace of her every movement.

Chris had referred to her as a siren. Certainly, she was that, but sirens, he recalled, were known to lure men to disaster.

Turning away, he devoted himself to his host, replying frankly to Mr Grantham's questions about his family and his own ambitions.

'Shall you follow your eldest brother into politics?' the old man enquired. 'I hear that the Earl of Brandon is well thought of in the highest circles. He is a member of the Government, is he not?'

'You have heard of him?' Perry was surprised. He had not mentioned Frederick, and wondered how Mr Grantham knew of the connection.

'Of course. A man of such gifts is spoken of, even here in Genoa. You have not answered my question, Mr Wentworth.'

Perry laughed. 'I have no taste for politics, sir, and my family would shudder at the thought of it. Sebastian, my second brother, assures me that I am no diplomat. He's right, of course...I am too impulsive.'

'Then the navy is to be your life?'

'I hope so.' Perry was launched upon his favourite

subject, but then he recalled his obligations to the ladies, and joined in the general conversation.

Later, after Mrs Grantham had retired, the gentlemen joined Elizabeth in the salon. Then, to his dismay, Perry found himself alone with her. He could not welcome the situation, but Chris had expressed an interest in Mr Grantham's pictures, and had been invited to examine them more closely. The look of reproach on Perry's face brought a wicked grin from Chris. He knew quite well that common politeness would require his friend to bear Elizabeth company.

'You do not care for paintings, Mr Wentworth?' She enquired stiffly.

'Chris is the expert, ma'am. I know nothing about them.'

'Indeed?' Her cool tone indicated that she found him little more than a barbarian.

Stung, he was quick to reply. 'You are a lover of the arts, Miss Grantham?'

'I have been brought up to value beautiful things.' The sarcasm in his voice had brought a glint of anger to her eyes. 'For some of us, there is more to life than learning to order men about, even aboard ship.'

'Really? You surprise me. I had supposed that nothing would please you more.'

'You may suppose whatever you will,' she answered coldly. 'That is, as long as you keep your opinions to yourself. You do not know me, Mr Wentworth. As far as I'm concerned that suits me very well. My hope is that our brief acquaintance ends this evening.'

Perry bowed. 'For once we are in full agreement, ma'am.'

'Oh!' she cried. 'You are impossible! You, sir, are the rudest, most arrogant creature I have ever met.'

'Again I must return the compliment, Miss Grantham.'

Elizabeth took a step towards him. Her eyes were blazing, and her small fists were clenched. 'If I were a man, I'd call you out for that!'

'Then let us be thankful that you are nothing more than a spoilt child.'

He thought she would explode with rage. Her hand closed about a valuable vase.

'No, don't throw it!' he advised. 'As a lover of beautiful things, you will not care to smash it.'

It was only with a supreme effort that Elizabeth regained her self-control. She sat down suddenly and began to drum her fingers on a nearby table.

'What a charming guest you are! One can only be thankful that you spend your life at sea, shouting your insults to the wind. There, they will have no effect.'

Perry was strongly tempted to box her ears. He opened his mouth to reply and then fell silent as his host returned.

Mr Grantham beamed upon his guests. 'Well, Puss, we must thank our friends for a most delightful evening, don't you agree? We entertain so little,' he explained. 'Elizabeth, poor darling, knows few young people. We do not go about as much as she would like. This has been a new experience for her.'

Perry said all that was polite, but he was in no doubt that it was one which Elizabeth would not care to repeat. To his surprise, Mr Grantham appeared to notice nothing amiss.

Chris was not so easily deceived, but it was not until he and Perry were walking back towards the docks that he voiced his suspicions.

'Another quarrel, old chap?'

'What else?' Perry's tone was savage. 'That girl is a harridan!'

'No, no! That's coming it too strong. You rub her the wrong way, that's all. It ain't like you, Perry. What happened to our handsome sailor who has the ladies falling at his feet?'

Perry eyed him darkly. 'Watch it!' he advised. 'A facer won't improve your looks.'

'Have mercy!' Chris pretended to quake with fright. 'Would you hit a man who is half your size?'

Perry's face cleared. 'Don't be such an ass!' he chuckled. 'I ain't in the best of humours, I'll admit, but the beautiful Miss Grantham tries my patience.'

'At least you ain't indifferent to her. It must be the first sign of love—' He dodged as Perry aimed a blow at him. 'What did she do this time?'

'It was her damned impertinence.' Perry could contain himself no longer. 'Insults, if you please, from a chit just out of the schoolroom.'

'But why?' Chris persisted. 'The evening seemed to go so well.'

'It did, until you insisted on examining those pictures. Why did you leave me alone with her?'

'Just giving you a chance, old thing. Besides, the old man was determined on it. It was his suggestion.' Chris began to laugh. 'I think he sees you as a prospective son-in-law.'

'Rubbish! He was doing the polite.'

'No, I see it all now. You are destined for the fair Elizabeth. Such a pity that I didn't stake my claim before you!'

'You are welcome to her. It ain't too late. You may woo her with my compliments, and I wish you joy of the lady. I'd as soon shackle myself to the Witch of Endor.'

'No need to trouble yourself,' Chris announced. 'We'll be gone before the week is out. I doubt if we'll see any member of that family again.'

This prophecy was not destined to be fulfilled, though Chris was right in his supposition that the *Artemis* was almost ready to sail. Two days before their departure, Perry received a letter from Mr Grantham. He opened it and read it with a groan.

'What is it?' Chris demanded. 'A letter from your lady-love? She has forgiven you?'

Perry handed over the letter. Its contents made Chris whistle in surprise.

'He can't be hoping still that you'll persuade the captain to change his mind?'

'I don't know,' Perry said heavily. 'I thought I'd convinced him that it was impossible.'

'Shall you go?'

'I suppose I must. He doesn't suggest a meeting at his home, thank God, but at the customs-house.'

'He may have a present for you...wine, perhaps...or brandy?'

'Possibly. I hope he won't go on about his daughter's safety. She could take on the revolutionary armies on her own.'

'Bear up, old chap! It may not be as bad as you suppose.'

It was worse. Though Mr Grantham greeted Perry with his usual warmth, he seemed to find some difficulty in broaching the subject uppermost in his mind.

Behind the smile, Perry saw that his eyes were sick with fear. His hands, spotted with the brown flecks of age, were shaking.

'My dear sir, what is it? Have you had bad news? Your wife is not worse, I hope?'

Mr Grantham shook his head. 'I cannot shake off the memory of the massacre of Toulon. Mr Wentworth, Elizabeth is the child of my heart. She must be saved.'

'But sir, I have explained…we cannot take her with us.' Moved by his companion's anguish, Perry's voice was gentle.

'Your captain will change his mind, I think, when he knows that there is a precedent. The British fleet has rescued many thousands—'

'Mr Grantham, under Admiral Hood, the fleet is at full strength. We are but a single ship, under special orders to make all haste to England. We must be a likely target for attack. The captain will not have women aboard, especially a young girl, unprotected as she must be, and among men who are not noted for their…er…restraint.'

Mr Grantham was silent for some moments. When he spoke again, it was clear that he was labouring under the stress of strong emotion.

'Will you sit down?' he asked in a low voice. 'I have thought of a solution.'

'Sir?'

'I will offer you my daughter's hand in marriage.'

'What!' The colour drained from Perry's cheeks. 'Forgive me! I think I cannot have understood you.'

'I am asking that you take Elizabeth to wife. That is, unless you have some previous attachment...?'

The temptation to lie to him was overwhelming, but Perry could not do it.

'It is not that,' he said slowly. 'Sir, you cannot have considered. You do not know me. Would you entrust your daughter to my care on the strength of a few meetings?'

'My dear boy, I have not lived for more than seventy years without becoming a judge of character. Besides, I knew your mother slightly many years ago, before she married Brandon. I have made enquiries, Mr Wentworth. I am satisfied that Elizabeth will be safe with you.'

# Chapter Three

Perry thought he must be dreaming. The old man's suggestion was too fantastic to be within the bounds of reality. That blow to the head must have addled his wits. He tried to hide his dismay.

'Have you spoken to your daughter on this subject, Mr Grantham?'

'No, I have not. She is too young to make such decisions for herself. She does not understand my worries.'

'Then she is certain to oppose this plan. Sir, there must be many worthy men in Genoa…'

'How would that help me? I want to send Elizabeth to England.' The old man looked at Perry's stricken face. 'What is your objection, Mr Wentworth? You have seen my girl. You need not fear her breeding, and she is not ill favoured…'

'She is beautiful,' Perry murmured. 'But the idea is preposterous.'

'But why? Forgive me. Perhaps I should not mention it but, as my only child, Elizabeth is my heir. Her dowry will be large…'

Perry flushed. 'That does not weigh with me,' he said with dignity.

'Then I do not understand.'

'Well, sir, if you will have the truth of it, I believe your daughter has taken me in dislike.' It was not the most tactful of replies, but Perry was growing desperate.

To his astonishment, Mr Grantham laughed. 'Have you been teasing her, my boy?'

Perry was silent. Without betraying Elizabeth's meeting with the Count, he could not explain.

'Won't you make allowances for her youth? I know she can be hasty, but at heart she is the best of girls.'

'But that's just it—' Perry was clutching at straws '—she is too young to be married.'

'Not so, my dear young man. And there is a precedent. Your Captain Fremantle was married aboard ship to Miss Betsy Wynne. She was the same age as Elizabeth.'

'But sir, they loved each other—'

'And you think you could not grow to love my child? That is difficult for a father to understand. You disappoint me, Mr Wentworth.'

'I am sorry to have to do so, but it cannot be.' Perry could imagine Captain Robsart's reaction if he were asked to conduct such a ceremony. 'Believe me, I should like to help you, but Miss Grantham and I should not suit.'

The old man eyed him sadly for some moments. Then, apparently resigned to defeat, he picked up his cloak and hat. 'I see that there is nothing more to be said. You must excuse me for troubling you once more.'

'I'm sorry, sir. I appreciate your trust in me.'

Mr Grantham nodded. Then he held out his hand. 'I wish you fair winds, and a safe journey back to England.'

With that he limped away, leaving Perry a prey to a mass of conflicting emotions. The strongest of these was an overwhelming feeling of relief.

It had been an uncomfortable interview, but thank heavens he had not retreated. The old man had allowed his fears to cloud his judgement. His plan could only have been born of desperation.


Later that evening he said as much to Chris.

'What did I tell you?' After an initial whistle of astonishment, Chris began to chuckle. 'I knew the old man had his eye on you. I can't believe that you turned him down, when you had the heiress in your pocket. You must be touched in the upper storey. Never suspected you of being such a slow-top, old chap.'

'I'm not the one who is touched in the upper storey. That blow to the head must have done more damage than we thought. To offer his daughter to a stranger? It is incredible!'

'Oh, I don't know,' Chris murmured slyly. 'You ain't a bad catch, old thing…aside from being a pretty face, I mean.'

'Determined to lose your front teeth, are you?' Perry advanced upon his friend.

Still laughing, Chris dodged behind a table, beyond the reach of those outstretched arms.

'Think about it,' he pleaded. 'Didn't old Grantham say he knew your mother?'

'What has that to say to anything?'

'Well, he don't strike me as a fool. He must have made enquiries about you. I can't think what's stopping you from taking the lady to your bosom.'

Perry glared at him. 'For one thing I detest her, and for another, I'll choose my own wife, thank you.'

Chris shook his head. 'When will you get another chance like this? The girl has everything to recommend her...youth...beauty...and a fortune with it.'

'Everything, in fact, but a pleasant disposition.'

'Damme, Perry, are you looking for some little mouse who'll hang about your neck, agreeing with your every word?'

'I'm not looking for anyone, and I won't be hustled into marriage to suit Mr Grantham.' Suddenly, his face cleared. 'Don't know why I'm going on,' he said more cheerfully. 'The girl herself would never have agreed.'

Chris emerged from behind the table. 'It's a pity, all the same. Tell you what! Suppose I try my luck?'

'This is no joking matter,' Perry said severely.

'I suppose not. In any case, I ain't sure that I want a wife just yet.' He couldn't resist a last gibe. 'At your age, though, it's time you were giving it some thought?'

'I'm not too old to deal with you, my lad. Ain't it time you went on watch?'


For the next two days they were kept fully occupied with preparations for their departure. Stores were late in arriving, fresh provisions were in short supply, and in the final hours before they sailed Perry was sent ashore with a small party to search for a couple of deserters. A fruitless search of several taverns didn't improve his mood.

'Damn their eyes!' he muttered savagely. 'We'll have to leave them. We can't miss the tide...'

The prospect of explaining to Captain Robsart that he would be forced to sail short-handed wasn't pleasant, and it was with some relief that he spied the two delinquents in a dockside haunt. Both men were the worse for drink, and incapable of walking to the ship unaided. He motioned to their shipmates to support them, and led the party back to the *Artemis*.

Ordering his captives to be taken to the brig, Perry made his way on deck and reported to the captain.

Behind his back, Captain Robsart was known as 'Hedgehog'. In truth, he bore a strong resemblance to that small and prickly creature. Beneath a head of stiff, grey bristles a pair of fierce eyes glared out at his first lieutenant. He gave a grunt, which might, or might not, have been one of approval. Then he turned away to deal with the task of seeing his vessel safely out of harbour. It was not until they had cleared the breakwater that he went below.

With their course set for Gibraltar, Perry remained on deck to take the watch. As the city of Genoa faded into the distance, he could only feel relieved. The strange events of the past few days could now be forgotten. He lifted his face to the breeze. How good it was to feel the rolling deck beneath his feet once more. He thought with pity of those who had never been to sea. They would never know his present sense of freedom.

Then he felt a pang of conscience. Was Mr Grantham watching their departure? The old man would be in despair, feeling that his last hope had gone.

Yet surely his fears were groundless? In time he would give his daughter's hand to one more worthy to receive it. Even so, he wondered what would be their fate.

Lost in thought, he did not notice the passing of the hours, but at last he was relieved. As he went below he found Chris waiting for him.

'You look as if you could do with a drink, old chap. Ain't you going to allow me to sample some of the wine you bought in Genoa?'

'As long as you remember that I'd like to reach England with at least a cask or two...'

'I'll stock you up at Gibraltar. Spanish brandy ain't too bad, and they run it across the border.'

With this assurance, he followed Perry into the latter's cabin. Then he paused in astonishment.

'I know we may be attacked, old thing, but did you really feel obliged to buy a coffin?'

Perry was equally startled by the sight of a narrow basketwork container, fully six feet in length, which took up most of what little space there was.

'What's this? It ain't mine.' Perry strode to the door and shouted for the cabin boy.

'Bosun brought it aboard, sir.'

'Then you'd best send him to me, and be quick about it. Damn it! There ain't room to swing a cat in here. The man must have lost his wits.'

He said as much to the bosun. 'What's this, Caxton? Whoever owns it, it should have been stowed in the hold.'

'It came from a Mr Grantham, sir. He was most

insistent that it was delivered to your cabin.' Caxton found it unnecessary to mention the sum of money which had accompanied this request.

Perry regarded him with a kindling eye. 'You did not feel it necessary to consult me?'

'You were busy, sir. Besides, the crate is mighty heavy. It took two of the men to fetch it from the deck.'

'He must have sent you one of his statues,' Chris announced. 'You lucky dog!'

Perry shook his head as he looked at the basket-work container. 'He'd have packed a statue in a wooden crate.' A thought too terrible to contemplate sprang unbidden to his mind. He brushed it aside. The idea was unthinkable. 'Possibly it is fruit,' he murmured. 'Very well, Caxton, you may go. I'll take a look at it. The men may remove it later.'

As the bosun left them, Perry looked across at Chris.

'Ain't you going to open it?' his friend enquired. 'I'll lay you odds that it ain't fruit. Why would he send you oranges and lemons? It must be books... The damp in the hold would ruin them.'

Perry did not answer him. He was staring at the box, and a sense of dread possessed him.

'Come on!' Chris was impatient to solve the mystery. 'Why are you so reluctant? It ain't likely to be filled with poisonous snakes, even if you did refuse to wed his daughter.'

Slowly, Perry fumbled with the leather straps. As they fell away he laid his hand upon the lid, but he could not bring himself to lift it.

Laughing, Chris pushed him aside. Then, as the lid fell back, both men stood as if turned to stone.

Chris was the first to find his voice. 'Good God!' he whispered. 'If it ain't the siren herself!'

It was true. Elizabeth lay curled in the heavily padded interior, swaddled tightly in a fine silk shawl. A light veil covered her face, which was further protected by a cobwebby mesh secured above her. She appeared to be asleep.

The shock robbed Perry of all power of speech. He staggered to a chair, put his head in his hands, and groaned.

'What will you do?' Chris laid a hand upon his shoulder. 'We can't turn back.'

'I don't know. My God! What has possessed the man? How could he do this to me?'

'He must have been desperate.' Chris had lost his usual ebullience. 'We had best tell the captain. Perhaps he'll put her ashore…'

'Alone, and on the coast of France? Of course he won't. Her father would rely on that. Damn the man! I wish I'd never set eyes on him…or his daughter!'

'Too late to think of that. Perry, it ain't your fault that she's aboard. The captain must see that.'

'He won't,' Perry told him in despair. 'He'll think I disobeyed his orders. I'll probably be court-martialled and strung up from the yardarm…'

There was a pause as both young men considered this gloomy prospect. Then Chris looked at his friend with sparkling eyes.

'We could hide her,' he suggested. 'Captain Robsart need not know.'

'Down here, and for weeks? Have you run mad?'

'I mean until we reach Gibraltar. There, we might be able to smuggle her ashore—'

'To make her own way back to Genoa? It can't be done.'

'Someone might take her in…the Governor, for example.'

'Not without a lot of explanations, which would be certain to reach the captain's ears. Besides, you've met her. As soon as she wakes up she'll start to scream and yell and make a fuss. Every man aboard will hear her.'

'Not if you keep her quiet…'

'And how do you suggest that I do that?'

'I don't know.' Chris strolled over to look at their unwelcome guest. 'Strange that she's still asleep…'

'She must be drugged, you idiot! For heaven's sake, don't try to rouse her. I can't cope with hysterics. Oh, God! What a mess! I can't think of a way out of it. There's nothing for it but to tell the captain.'

'No, Perry, stop and think! If he won't believe your story, it could be the end of your career. You don't wish to be drummed out in disgrace, do you? It wouldn't be so difficult to hide her.'

'With the cabin boy coming in and out? Do you imagine that he'd overlook her?'

'You could lock your door…'

'And why would I do that?'

'Valuables, old chap. In Genoa you bought gold trinkets for your family, and you don't wish to put temptation in the way of the men.'

Perry gave him a sour look. 'Any more ideas? Where am I to sleep, for example?'

'We do watch and watch about. You could use my cabin.'

For the first time, Perry was tempted. Perhaps he

could force himself to face the wrath of Captain Robsart, but all his hopes of preferment would be lost. It might be better to conceal Elizabeth's presence on the *Artemis*. Even if she were to be discovered later, he would be no worse off.

Sunk in gloom, he nodded his assent. 'We could try it,' he said slowly. 'I can't think of an alternative. Damn the woman! I could wish her far enough—'

As if she had heard him, Elizabeth began to stir. Perry was on his feet at once.

'Give me a hand,' he said briefly. 'Let's take this mesh away. She's still drowsy, but if she tries to scream I want to be able to stop her.'

As they disengaged the makeshift protective cage, Elizabeth's eyes opened. She stared up at them in disbelief, and a cry issued from her lips.

Perry clapped a hand across her mouth. 'Stop that!' he ordered. 'You must be quiet. We'll help you to your feet, and then I'll explain.'

He reached down, took her in his arms, and carried her over to the single chair.

Elizabeth struggled to stand, but her legs would not support her.

'Ma'am, you are still cramped,' Chris told her kindly. 'Will you not sit down until you feel more yourself?'

In silence, Perry poured a glass of water and held it to her lips. She took a sip and choked a little, but the drink restored her senses.

'What is this place?' She was obviously bewildered. 'Why am I here?'

'Miss Grantham, if you are patient, Perry will explain.' Chris looked at his friend.

'Oh!' she cried. 'You have kidnapped me, you villain!'

Perry responded stiffly. 'I assure you, madam, nothing could be further from the truth. Your presence here is a severe embarrassment, but this is your father's doing.'

'I don't believe you!' She almost spat the words at him. 'How dare you make such an accusation?'

'Unfortunately, it is true, Miss Grantham.' Chris spoke in soothing tones. 'He approached the bosun to have you brought aboard.'

'Aboard?' Elizabeth looked shaken. 'You mean that I am on your ship?'

Perry bowed. 'And on your way to Gibraltar, ma'am.'

'But I don't wish to go there,' she cried fiercely. 'Kindly put me ashore at once. I won't stay here.'

'You have no choice, Miss Grantham, unless you can walk on water. We sailed from Genoa some hours ago.' Perry did not trouble to hide his anger.

'Then your captain must return there. This is some mistake. Kindly take me to him.'

'Captain Robsart won't change course, so you need not get upon your high ropes. Your father has placed me in a most unfortunate situation.'

'Is that all that concerns you? I might have expected it. What of my situation? My father is sick. He must have been, to think of such a plan. That blow upon the head has sent his wits a-wandering. Oh, why did I not see it?' For a few seconds she looked distraught. Then her chin came up. 'Where are you supposed to take me?'

'To England, ma'am.'

'To England?' Her voice rose to a shriek. 'I won't

go there. Wait until Cesare hears of this. I am betrothed, you know—'

'You are *not* betrothed,' Perry said firmly. 'Your father made that clear to me. You do him an injustice. He is concerned only with your safety.'

'He need not be.' She stopped, unwilling to criticise her beloved parent. 'He imagines dangers which don't exist,' she murmured as if to herself. 'But I must go back.' She looked at Perry with a challenge in her eyes. 'Is there no way?'

'None, Miss Grantham.'

She gave him a stormy look. 'I don't believe you. I will see your captain—'

'No, you won't. Just be quiet, will you?'

Elizabeth stared at her companions. Then she understood. A smile of pure mischief curved her lips. 'An unfortunate situation, I think you said? Confess it, gentlemen, you are at a stand. Shall you be cashiered if I am found here?' The thought appeared to give her immense satisfaction.

'Of course not,' Perry told her sternly. 'The bosun is our witness. He brought you aboard.'

'With instructions to deliver me to your cabin? What will your captain say to that, I wonder? I understood from my father that he had refused me passage on the *Artemis*. Will he believe that you had no hand in this? I think not, especially if I convince him otherwise.'

'Why, you little wretch!'

Elizabeth smiled at him in triumph. Then she settled herself more comfortably in her chair and began to smooth her crumpled skirt.

'I am still a little dizzy, sir. Perhaps my morning

chocolate was drugged. I should welcome some refreshment…perhaps some fruit?'

Chris tumbled over his own feet in his anxiety to
obey her.

'Thank you so much.' Elizabeth selected a peach.
'Now, what is to be done, I wonder?'

Perry eyed her askance. He was under no illusions. With her quick intelligence the girl had seen
at once that she held them in her power. At a word
from her they were more than likely to be put in
irons. It was with a strong sense of foreboding that
he awaited her next move.

'Where is your next port of call?' she addressed
herself to Chris.

'Gibraltar, ma'am…but we can't put you ashore
there. You could not make your own way back to
Genoa.'

'It would be difficult,' she agreed meekly. 'And
in the meantime?'

'Miss Grantham, if you would consent to stay
here in Perry's cabin?'

'You mean to hide me? Will that not present you
with some difficulty? How are you to feed me?'

Perry scowled at her. A normal female would
have fallen into strong hysterics at the suggestion.
She had not asked the obvious question as to where
he was to sleep. It had not occurred to her.

Chris was ready with an explanation. 'Perry and
I share watch and watch about, ma'am. We shall use
my cabin. As to food…I expect that we shall manage.'

Elizabeth gave him her most enchanting smile. 'I
still believe that I should see your captain. You may

be mistaken. If I explain the circumstances, he may return to Genoa.'

'He won't!' Perry told her roughly. 'We are carrying urgent dispatches for the Admiralty in London, and time is of the essence.'

'I understand,' she told him sweetly. 'Then there is no more to be said. Pray do not worry about me, gentlemen. I shall be as quiet as a mouse. Now, if you will be good enough to lock the door behind you...'

It was a clear dismissal, and they had no option but to leave her.

'I thought she took it all very well,' Chris murmured. 'Poor creature! What a thing to happen to her! Perry, you are unfair to her. She was so reasonable.'

'Too reasonable by half. She's up to something. Didn't you see that smug expression? She looks like a cat with the cream. She'll make us jump, you mark my words.'

'You don't understand her,' Chris said with conviction. 'Must you paint her so black? She's a sweet little thing, and I feel sorry for her.'

'Don't waste your sympathy! Sweet? That isn't a word I'd use to describe her. If I'm not mistaken, that fertile little brain is at this moment plotting mischief.'

He was not far out in his reasoning. Elizabeth's initial reaction of helpless fury and frustration had been followed by a strong determination to escape from the *Artemis*.

She had, as yet, no idea how this might be accomplished, but it must take place at Gibraltar. Wentworth would not help her. He disliked her as heartily as she disapproved of him. Lord Christopher was her only hope. She had seen the admiration in his eyes. With a little encouragement he might be persuaded to fall in with her wishes.

She would give much to outwit Wentworth. He was a detestable creature. It was strange that her father had taken such a liking to him. Now, she supposed, the first lieutenant of the *Artemis* might have the effrontery to feel responsible for her. She began to giggle, knowing how much he longed to box her ears. He longed to be rid of her, she knew that well enough, but if he could, he would thwart her plans.

Meantime, she had no objection to making him squirm.

Besides, this was an adventure, however much she might rail against the unceremonious way she had been taken from her home and brought aboard.

In Genoa, she had longed for some excitement…some relief from the tedium of her daily life. Drawing and music lessons, and walks in the company of her governess, were no substitute for life in the great world.

She was a woman grown, but her father could not see it. Then Cesare had begun to woo her. The fact that his suit was frowned on by her father only lent a certain spice to their secret meetings.

She loved him dearly, and she *was* betrothed, in spite of Wentworth's dismissive words. It was just that one could not think of Cesare all the time.

At this moment, for example, it seemed more important to examine the contents of that curious box. She lifted out the folded silk, and found with satisfaction that some of the padding beneath her consisted of her warmest gowns and a woollen cloak.

She did not recognise the leather valise, but when she opened it she found that it contained undergarments, her toothbrush and combs, and best of all, a heavy purse filled with golden coins. That, she tucked into the pocket of her skirt, determined not to mention it. Let Wentworth think her penniless. That way, he would believe her less likely to escape.

For escape she would, but it would take careful planning. To travel through Spain and France was out of the question. She must take ship for Genoa. Some master of a merchant vessel would carry a passenger in exchange for gold.

First, there would be the problem of leaving the *Artemis* unobserved. Elizabeth frowned. It would be difficult for a woman. Then she remembered an idle comment made by Cesare when the British vessels came into port. Had he not sneered about the drabs who were allowed aboard? In their midst she might escape detection.

Meantime, she could do nothing until they reached Gibraltar. Perhaps an appeal to Captain Robsart? She dismissed the idea at once. From what she had heard, he would probably lose no time in placing her under the supervision of some British official, and that would delay her escape.

It was a pity. What a pleasure it would have been to expose the hateful Mr Wentworth to the full fury of his commanding officer. Sadly, she must forgo that joy. There was no point in adding to her difficulties.

She returned to the task of lifting out her clothing. Apart from the woollen cloak, her other garments were badly crumpled. She laid them on the bunk and smoothed the gowns as best she could.

Then, beneath the last of the garments, she saw a glimpse of white. It was a letter, addressed in a familiar hand. She snatched at it eagerly, praying that it contained some glimmer of hope. Wentworth might have lied to her. Perhaps her father did not intend her to go to England after all. At least it might contain some explanation, some word that she was to be put ashore at Gibraltar.

The missive was sealed, and with a sinking heart she gazed at the direction. It was addressed to Peregrine Wentworth.

Sorely tempted, she weighed it in her hand. He need never know that it existed, and it was vital that she knew the contents. Her father might have mentioned the gold, and without it she would be helpless. She fingered the seal, but she was loath to break it.

With a sigh, she laid the letter aside. It was sheer folly to allow such moral scruples to stand in her way in her present situation. If she were to carry out her plan, she must acquire a ruthless streak.

Perhaps she might divide the gold. If her father had not mentioned the amount, she could keep at least one half of it. After all, it was meant for her, in an indirect way.

She stifled a feeling of guilt and divided the coins into two piles, returning one of them to the leather purse. The other she tied securely in her handkerchief and tucked it into her pocket.

Then she heard Peregrine's voice.

'Leave it, lad!' he ordered. 'On this voyage my cabin will be locked. I have some valuables, you understand.'

'But, sir…your clothes?'

'I'll give them to you as necessary. Off you go!' The key turned in the lock, and Perry entered the cabin.

His eyes swept the tiny space. Then he scrutinised her closely.

'I'm still here,' she snapped. 'Did you expect me to vanish through the port?'

'You'd have a long swim back to shore. What's this?' He pointed to the letter.

'It's for you,' Elizabeth said shortly. 'I found it among my clothing.'

'And you didn't open it? You surprise me!'

'You must not judge everyone's morals by your own,' she replied.

Perry glanced at her, but he picked up the letter, broke open the seal, and carried it to the light.

'May I see it?' Elizabeth held out her hand, and rather to her surprise he did not argue.

Though the letter was brief, it was succinct. Mr Grantham apologised for the ruse, but he reiterated his determination to send his daughter to a place of safety. Elizabeth was to be delivered into the care of her aunt, in London. The gold was mentioned only in the hope that the unspecified amount would be sufficient. The letter ended with renewed thanks, and a loving message for his daughter.

As Elizabeth read those last few words her tears welled up, but she fought them back. The hated Mr Wentworth must not be given the satisfaction of seeing her in distress.

Why had her father taken such a step? If only he had waited. If his fears of an invasion proved groundless, she need not have been sent away.

Though her eyes were suspiciously bright, she

faced Perry squarely. 'I'm thirsty,' she said coldly. 'I should like a glass of wine.'

To her fury, he laughed. 'You are much too young to think of drinking wine.'

'On the contrary, sir. In Italy we take wine from an early age. You will find none of your puritanical English notions there.'

'And none in England either. You are behind the times. The Puritans were ousted long ago. However, we still doubt the wisdom of giving strong liquor to a schoolgirl.'

Elizabeth clenched her fists until her knuckles whitened. He was baiting her deliberately. It was only with a supreme effort that she kept her temper.

She picked up the bag of gold and tossed it to him. 'There, you have been paid. Now I should like some food, unless you intend to starve me.'

Perry's face grew dark with rage. He threw the money back at her. 'Keep it!' he told her savagely. 'You won't starve, Miss Grantham, though in my opinion you should have been drowned at birth.'

'More of your barbaric notions?' Elizabeth moved towards a cupboard. 'Now where do you keep your wine?' She picked up a bottle and examined the label. 'This will do. Will you be good enough to open it?'

Baffled, he snatched it from her, but he didn't refuse to fill her glass.

Elizabeth took a sip. She didn't like it much, but she wasn't about to say so. 'And the food?' she asked sweetly.

Perry glared at her. 'I hope you like salt beef, Miss Grantham. In the navy we live upon it for weeks at a time.'

'So soon after leaving Genoa? What happened to your fresh provisions?'

'Perhaps you'd care for a menu, ma'am.'

'No, no, that won't be necessary.' Elizabeth smiled up at him. 'A little chicken and some fruit will suit me very well.'

Perry bowed. 'You have set my mind at rest,' he said with heavy irony. 'I felt at the very least you would insist on duckling and green peas.'

'In January, sir? I hope I am not so difficult. Come, I have not asked for ices, jellies, fruit creams, syllabubs, or even a tart, though naturally if they were available...?'

'They are *not* available,' Perry shouted. 'This is a warship, in case you had forgot. It will be difficult enough to smuggle food to you—'

'But not impossible, I hope. I should hate to have to summon up my last reserves of strength to call for help.'

Goaded beyond belief, he took a step towards her.

'I should like to wring your neck,' he snapped in desperation. 'I wish I'd never set eyes on you.'

'There, at least, we are in full agreement.' Elizabeth gave him a dagger-look, and turned away, but he saw that her lips were trembling.

'I'm sorry,' he said stiffly. 'Please forgive me. I should not have spoken as I did.' He looked at her bent head and was seized with an overwhelming urge to comfort her. He reached out a hand and laid it on her shoulder, but she whipped round like a tigress.

'Go away!' she cried. 'I hate you!'

# Chapter Four

Hurt and bewildered, Perry was at a loss, but Elizabeth did not spare him.

'Had you not been so very busy back in Genoa we should not have met. All this is due to your interference.'

'Not quite all, ma'am.'

She coloured then, remembering. 'I beg your pardon, Mr Wentworth, I am being unjust. After all, you saved my father's life…but, you see, had he not met you he would not have got this maggot into his head about sending me to England.'

The memory of her father brought fresh tears to her eyes, and Perry was not proof against them. The girl was human after all, he thought to his surprise.

'Don't worry about him,' he said gently. 'He will make a full recovery, especially since he now believes you to be safe.'

It was an olive branch of sorts, and Elizabeth accepted it as such. She gave him a faint smile.

'Safe unless we are attacked,' she murmured. 'What happens then?'

'We fight back, of course. Whatever happens, we

shall give a good account of ourselves. You must not be afraid. I'll come for you if there is any danger of us sinking.'

'You think an attack may be likely?'

'Not here in the Mediterranean. The British Fleet has cleared this sea of enemy shipping. In the Bay of Biscay it may be a different matter.' He stopped. In future he would guard his tongue. There was no point in frightening her.

He glanced at her face in trepidation, but her eyes were sparkling.

'You mean that we might be involved in a real engagement?'

'Don't raise your hopes,' he told her in crushing tones. 'Either way, you will see nothing of it. If you imagine that the French will rescue you, I advise you to forget it.'

She looked at him for a long moment. 'I hadn't thought of it,' she admitted frankly. 'But now that you mention the matter...'

'Must I remind you that you, too, must be considered an enemy of the French? What would be your fate as a prisoner-of-war?'

'Are not the French thought gallant as far as ladies are concerned?' Elizabeth studied him out of the corner of her eye, and a tiny smile played about her lips.

'They don't make exceptions when sending victims to Madame Guillotine.' His sharp rejoinder was brutally effective. Elizabeth's face paled, but she made a valiant effort to recover.

'I should claim to be Italian,' she told him coldly. 'It is the truth. I *am* Italian on my mother's side...'

'You might not be given the opportunity to explain, you little fool!' Perry ran his fingers through his tousled crop in a gesture of despair. 'Have you no sense at all? Damn it, girl! Would you walk into a hornet's nest?'

Belatedly, it occurred to him that this was not the way to speak to any female, however young.

'I beg your pardon for my language,' he said stiffly. 'But you would try the patience of a saint.'

'And that you are not. Pray don't apologise, Mr Wentworth. That would be out of character. Nothing in your behaviour has surprised me.'

'Thank you! You are too kind! If you will excuse me, Miss Grantham, I will see what can be done about some food for you.' Perry stalked away, with every line of his figure expressing his outrage at her words.

Did anyone ever get the better of her in a verbal encounter? he wondered bitterly.

'You ain't been doing battle again?' Chris looked at the glowering face. 'Perry, this ain't like you. Have you lost your sense of humour?'

'I don't find this situation amusing. That little wretch is the most exasperating creature in the world. I'd like to throw her over the side.' Perry caught his friend's eye and saw the laughter there. He was teased into a reluctant smile.

'You're right!' he admitted. 'I must be mad to pull caps with a stupid schoolroom miss. Now she is demanding fruit, chicken and a choice of pastries. She was kind enough to mention that ices and syllabubs were not essential. She would excuse me if they were not available.'

Chris gave a shout of glee. 'She's winding you up, old lad. Damme, if she ain't a complete hand!'

'Since you find all this so entertaining, perhaps you'd care to fetch the food?'

'Sorry, can't be done! I'm on duty. I'll leave it in your capable hands.' Still laughing, he made his way on deck.

Perry bent his mind to the problem of obtaining food without arousing suspicion. The officers dined together in the wardroom. In such close proximity it would be impossible to conceal anything about his person.

He wandered into the galley, to find the cooks preparing for the evening meal. Steaming cauldrons, securely lidded, hung from stout hooks, swaying with the rolling of the ship. A guard rail round the cooking surfaces prevented other utensils from sliding off to cast their contents over the sweating minions who pushed past him.

The cook raised an eyebrow in enquiry.

'Just a routine inspection, Hanley. The stores came aboard as ordered?'

'Yes, sir. Watch your uniform, Mr Wentworth. Grease stains will be the devil to get out of your whites.'

Perry turned away, carefully abstracting a couple of pieces of chicken from a tray intended for the wardroom. A kitchen cloth lay close to hand, so he threw it over them, pretending to use the cloth to wipe his cuff.

'Hanley, I'd like some fruit.'

'Certainly, sir. I'll have it sent to your cabin.'

'Don't bother. I'll help myself.' Perry took a generous amount and piled it on a plate.

So far so good, but obtaining food for his unwilling captive promised to become a problem. He could inspect the galley every day, but Hanley would be quick to notice pilfering. Some poor wretch was likely to be blamed and flogged.

He regained his cabin to find Elizabeth sitting by the port. As she turned to face him he noticed that all her colour had fled, and her skin bore a greenish tinge.

'There!' He laid the chicken on the plate, and set the fruit beside it. 'That's the best I can do.'

'Take it away,' she groaned. 'I think I'm going to die…'

'Seasick? Then come away from the port. Nothing is worse than watching the horizon. You had best lie on the bunk.'

For all that Perry had wished her to perdition, he felt a pang of pity. He helped her over to the pallet. 'Shall I take off your shoes?' he asked.

'Do as you please! Oh, I feel so dreadful…'

'Try to sleep,' he advised. 'When you get your sea legs you'll feel better.'

'Certainly I couldn't feel worse. Please go away. I think I'm going to be sick.' Elizabeth closed her eyes and turned her head away.

'No, you aren't,' Perry told her firmly. He filled a bowl with water and began to bathe her head. 'Don't think about it.' He brushed the curls back from her brow. 'You are in good company,' he told her lightly. 'Captain Nelson suffers with the same complaint each time he goes to sea, but he don't let it stop him.'

'He must be mad,' she groaned. 'Is there no remedy?'

'The best one is to sit beneath a tree.'

Elizabeth's eyelids flickered. 'How…? Oh, I see.

Mr Wentworth, this is no time for jokes. I should be happy to be put ashore.'

'Don't worry about it,' he murmured soothingly. 'Just close your eyes...' He began to stroke her brow. Then his long fingers moved to her temples at each side, making small circles with his fingertips.

'Ah, that feels so good!' she sighed. Within minutes she was sound asleep.

Perry left the cabin and locked the door behind him. The problem of providing food had been replaced by another. It hadn't occurred to him that Elizabeth might be taken ill. He couldn't care for a sick female, yet what was he to do? He cursed beneath his breath, and was immediately ashamed.

For the hundredth time he railed against the mischance which had taken him into Genoa on that fatal night. Then he shrugged. He could not change the situation now. He must make the best of it. It wasn't Elizabeth's fault that she was in his charge, and it couldn't be easy for her. Tonight she had looked so vulnerable...

It was in a gloomy frame of mind that he went on deck to relieve Chris. It was some time before his normal optimism returned. Then common sense persuaded him that a bout of seasickness was nothing. Elizabeth would soon recover. If she had broken an ankle or some such mishap, it would be a different matter. He would put her from his mind.

This was not so easily accomplished. Quiescent for once, her creamy skin had felt so soft beneath his fingertips. Watching her fall asleep, he had been struck once more by the ridiculous length of the dark lashes which rested against those smooth cheeks. And her mouth? Ah, that mouth! What must it be like to kiss those mobile, wilful lips, silencing all her protests?

Perry stopped his pacing of the quarterdeck and took himself to task. He was growing maudlin. Like Chris, he had been at sea too long. Deprived of female company, a man could not be blamed if his natural instincts surfaced on occasion.

He must watch himself. The child was in his care, and he would not betray her father's trust, however strongly tempted he might be.

He didn't even like Elizabeth, but he was wise enough to know that sometimes proximity was sufficient to arouse his baser feelings. In future, he would keep her at a distance.

Upon this worthy resolution he joined his fellow officers in the wardroom, only to find that he had no enthusiasm for their usual banter.

'Sorry to be leaving Genoa, Wentworth? Have you lost your heart to some Italian *signorina*? You are quiet tonight...' A grinning face greeted him from across the table.

'Nothing of the sort,' Perry replied in casual tones. 'I thought I'd leave the wit to you this evening.'

A howl of amusement greeted this remark.

'There's a leveller for you, Jordan. Come on now, give him his own.'

The object of their raillery was spared the need to reply as Captain Robsart joined them.

'Too much noise, gentlemen!' His black brows drew together in a frown. 'Try to contain your levity. We must concentrate on the business in hand.'

His words put a stop to any further joking. Each man knew that a question from his superior officer must be answered in full and without delay. When it came to naval strategy the captain's skills were famous. He expected a similar commitment from each member of his crew.

Fudging and stupidity brought down a blistering tirade of wrath upon the luckless recipient. Men had been known to remark that they would have preferred a flogging at the masthead.

Perry ventured only a single remark. 'Are we to join up with Admiral Hood, sir?'

'No, Mr Wentworth, we are not. The Fleet will stay here in the Mediterranean. The urgency of our mission means that we must make all haste to England.' The captain then confined his conversation to the need for daily practice by the gunnery crews. 'Too slow by half,' he announced with a glare at Chris. 'As gunnery officer, you will speed them up, sir, or I'll have the skin off their backs.' With this dire threat, he left them to deliberate among themselves.

Jordan whistled. 'Why the need for haste, I wonder? There must be something in the wind. I thought it couldn't be concern for our health which was taking us back to England. Still, mustn't look a gift-horse in the mouth...I'll be glad to get back.'

'To your loved one...and your wife?' someone asked slyly.

There was a ripple of amusement, and Jordan laughed. The high-flyer whom he had in keeping was no secret to his fellow officers.

'Jealous?' he asked blandly.

'Not at all! The lady would ruin me in a week. Still, if we chance upon a prize or two, I might give you a run for your money...'

As the conversation turned to prizes, Perry made his escape. Tomorrow he was due for a lengthy spell of duty, and he was badly in need of rest.

With his head upon the door of Chris's cabin he paused. Perhaps he should look in upon Elizabeth. It would take but a moment. He felt in his pocket for his key.

Elizabeth was still asleep. For a time he stood beside her, touched by the childish way she had curled up, one hand beneath her cheek. Some of her colour had returned, and he reached out a hand to touch the delicate peach-bloom of her skin.

He stopped himself in time. This was madness. He was about to turn away when he noticed that she had disturbed her coverlet. He picked it up and bent to throw it over her. At that moment her eyes opened.

'What are you doing?' she demanded fiercely.

Her tone annoyed him. 'I was trying to make you comfortable, ma'am. Don't worry! I have no designs upon your virtue.'

Elizabeth blushed to the roots of her hair. 'Don't be ridiculous!' she cried. 'Pray don't trouble yourself about my comfort. I feel much better now.'

'Then you will eat your chicken?'

Elizabeth glared at him. 'Certainly!' She avoided looking at the food.

'I must hope that it is to your taste. There is a pork stew today...though you may find it greasy.'

Elizabeth paled. 'Sir, you are the most detestable creature I have ever met!'

'Why is that?' Perry was all innocence. 'I merely suggested—'

'I know what you suggested. You think to make me ill again, but you will not do so.'

'No? Oblige me then, Miss Grantham, by eating the chicken. I was at some pains to bring it to you.'

'Go away!' she shouted. 'Whatever pains you suffered, they were not enough.'

'Cruel!' he told her solemnly. 'Most females are gentler in their ways.'

'This female is not!' She faced him with flashing eyes. 'Get out before I stab you with this knife.'

'Shall I leave it with you? Such a dangerous weapon!' He pretended to consider. 'It might be best if you ate the chicken with your fingers.'

'Just try to take it from me, Mr Wentworth. You'll regret it!'

Perry backed away. 'I shouldn't think of it, my dear young lady. You frighten me to death!' His laughing eyes belied his words, and served only to infuriate his listener further. 'Enjoy your meal!' With this parting shot he left the cabin.

The girl was the very devil, he decided. The temptation to be rid of her was strong. At Gibraltar he could help her to escape, if he could bring himself to do so. What bliss it would be to abandon his troublesome charge. He dismissed the idea as unworthy of an honourable man.

Difficult though she was, the child could not be left to fend for herself. He sighed. He was beginning to know Elizabeth well. Once ashore and out of his sight, she would go to any lengths to take passage back to Genoa.

Even if he spoke to Captain Robsart it would make no difference. The headstrong little chit would think of a dozen ways to elude the vigilance of any official who might be persuaded to give her shelter at the port.

'Lost in thought, old chap?' Chris was preparing to go on duty. 'How is our fair maiden?'

'Back on form. She suffered from the rolling of the ship, but it passed off... Now her tongue is just as sharp as ever...'

'Get some sleep!' Chris advised. 'I'll look in on her later with some books and a pack of cards. She must be bored, poor thing!'

'As you wish.' Perry tossed him the cabin key. 'She'll probably bite your head off.'

'No, she won't. I shall use my well-known charm...'

'And the best of luck to you!' Perry removed his jacket. 'I'll come for the body later.' With that he threw himself upon the bunk and closed his eyes.

Later, when he made his way to his own cabin he found a scene of perfect harmony.

'Miss Grantham has cleaned me out.' Chris held up his cards. 'I owe her thousands, though I believe she cheated.'

'No, I didn't,' Elizabeth's eyes were dancing. 'Sir, you should pay more attention to your hand.'

'How can I? Your beauty has undone me.'

'Don't be such a noddlecock, Lord Christopher!' Elizabeth ignored the compliment and shuffled the pack again. 'You must concentrate instead of chatting.'

Perry was amused. Whatever her other faults, this provoking creature wasn't vain.

'Please call me Chris,' his lordship pleaded. 'I hoped we might be friends.'

Elizabeth looked at him. Then her enchanting smile peeped out. 'Very well, but you must not accuse me of cheating.'

'My apologies, ma'am. I am jealous of your skill, you see.'

She laughed at that. 'I learned in a hard school. My father is an expert.'

'And you bid fair to follow him. Will you excuse me now? I have some matters to attend.' With that he hurried away.

Elizabeth looked troubled. 'Will he be reprimanded? I should not have kept him for so long...'

Perry shook his head. 'Chris is the gunnery officer. He must arrange for practice in the morning. Don't worry, he won't be keelhauled.'

'Keelhauled? What is that?'

'We tie a rope to the offender and throw him overboard. Then he is dragged beneath the ship and drawn up on the other side.'

'What a barbaric practice! I didn't know that the navy drowned its sailors.'

'Some of them survive,' he said with feigned uninterest. 'It need not concern you. I have not heard of a woman being keelhauled, although there is always a first time.'

Elizabeth glared at him. Then she saw the twinkle in his eyes.

'You're gammoning me,' she accused him with a reluctant smile.

'Just a little. Do you care to continue with this game of cards?' He seated himself on the edge of the bunk and began to shuffle the pack.

She looked her surprise, but the opportunity to beat him was too good to miss.

'Piquet?' he suggested.

She nodded, sure of her own ability. The corners of her mouth lifted.

Perry did not miss that look of triumph. He guessed correctly that the game was a favourite of her own. She was soon absorbed, studying her hand with total concentration. She played well, and he could understand why Chris had found her hard to beat. She spoke only once, to enquire about the stakes.

'Let us play for points,' he suggested. 'We may consider the forfeits later.'

Elizabeth leaned back in her chair, laying her hand face down. 'Do you think to trick me?' she asked calmly.

Perry assumed a look of injured innocence. 'How so?'

'I believe you hope to win. If so, the forfeit might be my promise not to escape.'

'I have no fear of that, Miss Grantham. We are far from land.'

'That won't always be the case.'

'Agreed, but it is enough to set my mind at rest for the present. Since you don't trust me, then let us play for oranges and lemons. Ten points for each, I think.'

She jumped to her feet at that. Her eyes were ablaze with anger, and her colour was high.

'I am not a child,' she cried. 'I have money...'

'So you keep reminding me. Aren't you satisfied with the thousands that you won from Chris?'

'We were only funning. It was just a game, pretending that we might play for high stakes.'

'This is not,' Perry said deliberately. 'I won't throw tricks your way.'

'And you think he did so?' She was furious. 'I thought he played to win.'

'You need have no such fears with me. I shall push you hard. Sit down, Miss Grantham! Success at cards needs a cool head.'

'There's no need to prose on at me in that superior way. What a bore you are!' In high dudgeon she picked up her hand again.

To be classed as a prosing bore was more than flesh and blood could stand. Perry was so irritated that his opponent was able to take the first points with ease. His temper was not improved by her evident delight.

She didn't speak to him again, reserving all her attention for the game, but by this time he was on his mettle. He settled down, determined to beat her, and his greater experience enabled him to take the next rubber.

Elizabeth could not hide her chagrin. 'Another?' she challenged.

Perry shook his head. 'You shall have your revenge another day.' He regarded her with interest. 'You should do well in London...'

'Why do you say that?'

'I was thinking of your skill at cards. Gambling is an obsession with the *ton*.'

'Even among the ladies?' Elizabeth gave him a limpid smile. Let him think her compliant. She knew better. She would never be taken to London.

'Especially among the ladies, ma'am. The married women gamble for the highest stakes.'

Perry expected a tirade, coupled with the assurance that if her relatives hoped to marry her off to some namby-pamby Englishman they would be making a sad mistake.

Instead she smiled again. 'How interesting!' she murmured.

Perry was undeceived. She had confirmed his belief that she intended to escape at the earliest opportunity, but his determination matched her own. Gibraltar was her only hope, and he would watch her like a hawk.

'Have you ever met your aunt?' he asked carelessly.

'No. I have lived in Italy all my life.'

'And the lady does not travel?'

'She travels extensively, so I understand, but she prefers the East.'

'Then you have no notion of her ways?'

'None.' Elizabeth looked thoughtful. 'Aunt Mary is childless and a spinster. I expect that she will be a stickler for convention.'

'I see.'

'Do you, Mr Wentworth? Can you imagine what it must be like to sit with folded hands, murmuring insipidities?'

Perry laughed aloud. 'You won't do that, I fancy.'

'No, I won't! Sometimes I wish that I'd been born a man.'

'You can't mean that. Is it because you have a craving for excitement? You may get more than you wish, here on the *Artemis*.'

'If we are attacked, you mean?'

'It could happen. I wonder how you will enjoy the noise of battle, the cries, the shouting and the falling timbers? Shall you not be afraid?'

'Shall you?' Elizabeth was stung by his scornful tone.

'I shall be too busy to think of anything but the task in hand.' He saw her look of disbelief and added calmly, 'For you it will be different. If we sight an enemy vessel I will unlock the cabin door, but you must not come on deck. Will you give me your word on that? You must stay here until I come for you.'

'Certainly not! Suppose you should be injured, sir? Am I to stay here even if the ship goes down?' The glint in her eye warned him that she intended no such thing.

'Chris knows that you are here,' Perry snapped. He'd hoped to frighten her into obedience, but he'd failed. The little wretch was untroubled by the thought that he might be felled by enemy fire.

In that he was mistaken. When he left, Elizabeth took herself to task. She had not been kind. If the truth were known, she had no wish to see him injured.

A vision of his mangled corpse swam before her eyes, and she found that she was trembling. Naturally, she would feel the same about any unlucky victim of the French.

Sternly she recalled her wandering thoughts. She must not allow her imagination to run away with her. An attack was unlikely, here in the Mediterranean. It was nonsense to indulge in foolish fancies. At Gibraltar she would leave the *Artemis*. After that, the fate of the vessel and her crew were no concern of hers.

There was still the problem of making her escape. The difficulties seemed almost insuperable. Perry never forgot to lock the cabin door behind him. She could strike him down with a blow from some heavy object if she could catch him unawares. Even then she had still to appear on deck in her own clothing, climb down the ship's ladder, and gain the dock unseen. If, as she hoped, the sailors' women were allowed aboard, she might lose herself in the crowd as they were leaving.

Otherwise she must have help. Lord Christopher had made his admiration clear. If she were clever, she might persuade him to fall in with her wishes. She would try him out, without mentioning her plans at first.

She might dwell upon her longing for fresh air, or the wish to feel firm ground beneath her feet again. She might even tease him into smuggling her ashore as a light-hearted escapade, simply to relieve the tedium of the voyage.


Her plan went well for the next few days. In Chris's company she exerted all her charm.

This put Perry on his guard at once. 'Take care!' he warned. 'Your fair Elizabeth is up to something. She's much too pleasant and amenable.'

Chris blushed. 'Must you always be so out of reason cross with her? I thought she was behaving very well.'

'Too well!' Perry said darkly. 'Just remember that she don't wish to be here. She'll get away if she can.'

'Stuff! How can she get away? You keep her locked below. Poor creature! She must be longing for a breath of air.'

'Then, Sir Galahad, why don't you open the port?'

'I will!' Chris was very much upon his dignity. 'I tell you, Perry, you are turning sour. It ain't her fault that she's aboard the *Artemis*.'

'Nor is it mine!'

'At least you weren't drugged and bundled into a basket. I admire her spirit. Why do you hold her in such dislike?'

'I don't trust her. Can't you see what she is doing? When did we last come to dagger-drawing, you and I? She's playing one of us against the other.'

'I don't believe that. You can't see any good in her.'

'Good grief! Is that it? Are you in love with her?'

The colour flooded Chris's face. 'I am,' he said quietly. 'You may keep your opinions to yourself. You shall not criticise my future wife.'

Perry whistled in disbelief. 'Has she agreed to wed you?'

'Not exactly,' Chris admitted in confusion. 'But I am encouraged to believe that...'

'That you may persuade her? Believe me, you will have no difficulty.'

'Perry, you need not sneer. I think the world of her. I know that you don't value her as I do, but you've been wrong about her from the start...' With that, he stalked away.

Perry went on deck. It was a fine night, with just enough breeze to fill the sails which billowed high above him. For once, he felt no pleasure in the gentle motion of the ship, or the stars which twinkled in the velvet sky.

His thoughts were savage. Damn the girl! Of all

the underhand tricks! She had no scruples of any kind. She didn't care for Chris, and to tease him into thinking that she did was the outside of enough. She was a heartless little wretch.

But he would best her yet. Her beauty wouldn't lull him into believing that she'd had a change of mind, or that she'd been transformed into a milk-and-water miss.

He smiled in spite of himself. Elizabeth certainly wasn't that. Honesty compelled him to admit that Chris was justified in his admiration of her spirit. She had not given way to hysterics, or fallen into a fit of the dismals. Far from it. She'd eaten such food as they could smuggle to her without complaint, and somehow, although he could not imagine how she did it, she had contrived to appear as well groomed as she did ashore.

Feeding her had been a problem. The consumption of fruit aboard the *Artemis* had increased sharply, but that would not give rise to comment.

Since Captain Nelson had discovered the value of oranges and lemons in the control of scurvy, all naval vessels carried plentiful supplies of the fruit, and the men were forced to eat it. Since then, the navy had not lost a single man to that dreaded scourge.

Grumbles were stilled when the crew realised that they need no longer suffer the appalling muscular pains, the lassitude, and the depression of the disease, which was so often fatal. It had added to the hazards of a lengthy voyage.

Certainly, Elizabeth would not suffer it, Perry thought wryly. She had the hearty appetite of a schoolgirl. When they reached Gibraltar he would go ashore, and lay in a store of provisions which she might keep in the cabin.

Then the humour of the situation struck him. He had railed at Chris for falling victim to the lady's charms when he himself was planning extra comforts for her. It was ridiculous, but naturally any gentleman must give some consideration to the weaker sex.

His smile broadened. Weaker? He'd back her courage against that of any man. With a shake of his head he went aft in response to a call from the helmsman.

'What is it?' he asked quietly.

'Over there, sir. I thought I saw a light.'

Perry peered into the darkness, but he could see nothing.

'Over there, Mr Wentworth...off the starboard bow.'

At that moment the moon appeared from behind a passing cloud. It revealed a number of small vessels riding at anchor, their lights strung out like a jewelled necklace against the far horizon.

'Looks like a fishing fleet,' Perry murmured. 'Most probably Spaniards, out of Almeria.'

'Then landfall tomorrow, sir?'

'If the wind holds fair. You have a brother serving at Gibraltar, I believe...?'

The man smiled. It was like Mr Wentworth to remember that. He knew every member of the crew by name, and never forgot to enquire about their families, unlike some officers he could name.

Perry strolled to the rail and gazed at the foaming wake as the vessel cleaved through the swell. He'd enjoyed his previous visits to the Rock, where he had many friends. This time it would be different. Tomorrow would be the danger point as far as Elizabeth was concerned.

Perhaps he should have another word with Chris. The girl would try to trick him if she could. He cursed his own lack of tact. He had said too much, and Chris would not believe him now.

One alternative was to beg a few drops of laudanum from the surgeon, but the thought of drugging her filled him with distaste. If she'd been a man, he could have found some pretext to have her clapped in irons, but that too was out of the question.

Perhaps if he spoke to her again, pointing out the folly of attempting a journey back to Italy on her own? It was a forlorn hope.

At this moment she was probably using all her charms on Chris to coax him into helping her with some mad scheme. She'd be cajoling, wheedling, possibly even allowing him to kiss her.

Perry's face grew so dark that the helmsman decided not to trouble him with further conversation. Young Mr Wentworth had a cheerful disposition, but something had upset him. The man shrugged. The gentry had their queer ways. Sometimes there was no knowing what maggot they got into their heads.

It would have surprised him to learn that his superior officer was suffering an attack of the blackest jealousy. Perry did not recognise it for what it was. The emotion was entirely new to him.

Like any other young man, he had fancied himself in love with a number of high-flyers. When they had moved on to pluck another pigeon he had taken the desertion in good part, often relieved to be free of the entanglement.

The thought of marriage had not crossed his mind. His mother had thrown young ladies in his way without success. None could compare with Prudence, his brother's wife. Cast into the shade by her forthright personality, they had seemed insipid.

There was a woman for you, he thought affectionately. Prudence was feisty, intelligent and courageous. He and she were the best of friends. She'd smile to see him mooning about like a lovesick calf.

Lovesick? No! It wasn't true! He stopped his pacing to grip the rail so tightly that his knuckles whitened in the moonlight.

If there was one woman in the world who could be guaranteed to bring out the worst in him, it was Elizabeth Grantham. They fought incessantly. She was spoilt, arrogant, bossy, and…and devious. He had never yet bested her in a verbal encounter. She had an answer for everything. He was merely suffering from irritation.

This was understandable. In time of war a naval officer must not be distracted by the tantrums of some chit of a girl. He would put her from his mind.

He then began to wonder what was taking place between Elizabeth and his friend in the cabin below.

He would not have found it a soothing sight. Chris was holding Elizabeth's hand, and whispering words of love into her willing ear.

# Chapter Five

'How beautiful you are tonight!' Chris said reverently. 'Elizabeth, I love you so. I'll do my best to make you happy if you will become my wife...'

Elizabeth looked up at him. 'Dear Chris, how can I give you an answer? I am so confused...I fear I am not myself at present.'

'Have I upset you? I didn't mean to do so. Have I spoken too soon?'

She gave him a tremulous smile. 'It is not that, but I was brought here against my will. I've tried to be brave, even though I am a prisoner in this cabin. The worst thing is that Mr Wentworth has taken me in such dislike. It has quite sunk my spirits. No matter what I do, I cannot please him.'

Chris scowled. 'He is unreasonable. I raked him over, I can tell you. He's much in need of a lesson in good manners.'

'Do you think so? I confess that I am tempted to play a trick on him.'

'That would be famous, and just what he deserves. But what can we do?'

'Suppose he were to find this cabin empty? Could

you hide me elsewhere? It would give him such a fright.'

'He'd go mad!' Chris looked doubtful. 'Besides, you might be seen by one of the crew. We have no women aboard.'

'But when we dock?' Elizabeth blushed prettily. 'Your captain does not permit visits by the women of the town?'

'My dear Elizabeth!' Chris coloured to the roots of his hair. It was a shock to discover that his paragon of purity and innocence had heard of the drabs who frequented the ports in the hope of earning a few coppers from men starved of female company.

'Now you are scandalised...I'm sorry.' Elizabeth hung her head in mock contrition. 'I would not have you think me guilty of vulgarity.'

'No, I don't! I mean, I was surprised, that's all. You are right, of course. The captain don't approve, but he's a realist, and turns a blind eye.'

'I could wear my hooded cloak,' Elizabeth cooed. 'No one need ever know.' She pressed his hand. 'Do say that you'll agree? It would be a famous joke...'

A glance at her companion's face told her that he was still doubtful. 'I see what it is,' she murmured. 'You fear Mr Wentworth's anger. Pray forget the matter. I should not have mentioned it.'

'Dearest, you may ask anything in the world of me.' Chris pressed her fingers to his lips. 'We'll do it. It need only be for an hour or so. Then we shall set his mind at rest.'

'Of course!' Elizabeth dimpled at him. 'Now we are conspirators!' Her sparkling glance encouraged him to try to kiss her, but she evaded him with ease.

'Not now!' she warned. 'Come to me tomorrow.'

Having dismissed him, she was satisfied. Once outside the cabin, she would slip away from him. Then, with any luck, she would be able to hide herself on the boat which took the women back to shore.

That night she slept like the proverbial log, untroubled by the need to make further plans. With money in her pocket, the future would take care of itself.

Next day she woke to find the *Artemis* at anchor in the shelter of Gibraltar's massive rock. She dressed quickly, impatient to carry out her plans. A glance through the porthole told her that the day was cloudy, with the promise of rain. Darkness would fall early on that January night.

Meantime, she must not betray herself. Perry must not suspect her plans.

That day he paid her only the briefest of visits, pleading the pressure of his duties. She nodded pleasantly. He did not know it, but he would not see her again.

As his key turned in the lock, she added another gown to the one she was already wearing. It made her feel uncomfortably bulky, especially when she tied the small satchel containing the purse of gold and a change of underthings beneath her skirt. She could carry nothing more, or even Chris would be suspicious.

Then all she could do was to wait.

The hours dragged endlessly, but it grew dark at last. Later, she heard laughter and the sound of female voices, the first she'd heard since leaving

Genoa. It gave her hope. Her captivity would soon be at an end.

It was long after midnight when Chris came for her. A glance at his troubled face told her that he still had doubts, but she made no comment beyond a cheerful greeting.

In silence he beckoned her through the open door, and hurried her along the passage.

'Going somewhere?' a deep voice enquired. Elizabeth looked up to see the hated Mr Wentworth smiling at her in triumph.

With an inarticulate cry of rage, she tried to slip past him, but he was too quick for her. Her wrist was seized in a vice-like grip, and she was bundled back into the cabin.

'Steady on, Perry! No need to be so rough, old chap. This was just a joke. We were planning to play a trick on you.' Chris had the grace to look ashamed.

'I ought to break your neck,' Perry said deliberately. 'I warned you, Chris. You may think this just a joke, but madam here does not.'

'That's right! Go on at her as usual!' In his anger Chris forgot to be defensive. 'How sour you are become! You used to enjoy a joke as much as anyone.'

'At this moment my sense of humour is a little strained.' Perry spun Elizabeth round and snatched the cloak from her shoulders. 'Look at her! Even you must see that she is ready for flight. Perhaps you think it the latest fashion to be wearing several garments?'

'Take your hands off my future wife, or you will answer to me!'

'Your future wife? Don't be such a fool! I think you have forgot Count Cesare di Tavola.'

'I have not forgot.' Chris was scarlet with anger. 'Elizabeth has explained. It was just a youthful infatuation.'

'So she is now in love with you?'

'You need not sneer. Rip up at her again, and you may name your friends.'

'With pleasure!' Perry bowed. His own anger threatened to choke him.

'Stop it, both of you!' Elizabeth was quick to intervene. 'You are behaving like a pair of idiots!'

'I'd use a stronger word for your own behaviour.' Perry rounded on her. 'Well, madam, have you promised to wed his lordship?'

'No, I haven't!' Elizabeth could not look at Chris.

'Oh, my dear, I thought it was settled between us—'

'No, Chris. Mr Wentworth is right, though it grieves me to say it. I have deceived you.'

'You mean that you only pretended to be fond of me?' The disconsolate expression on Chris's face cut her to the heart.

'That isn't so,' she told him in a low voice. 'I am fond of you, but not in the way that you might wish.'

'Honesty, at last?' Perry eyed her with undisguised contempt. 'Admit it, madam, you will use anyone to gain your ends.'

'Do you blame me?' Elizabeth was deeply ashamed, but she would not let him see it. 'I won't be taken to England...I won't!'

'Go to bed!' Perry ordered. 'By the way, I'll take that bag of gold.'

'I won't give it to you.'

'I think you will, unless you wish me to search you.'

Chris started forward with a furious word of protest, but Elizabeth stopped him with an uplifted hand.

'Your friend means what he says,' she said in icy tones. 'Nothing would give him greater pleasure than to humiliate me, but I won't allow it. Turn your backs!'

Both men turned away as she lifted her skirts. Then Perry staggered as the heavy purse struck him on the shoulder.

'You've got your way,' she hissed. 'Now get out!'

'Charming as ever!' Perry drawled. He motioned Chris ahead of him, pausing only to re-lock the door.

Elizabeth sat down suddenly, a prey to utter despair. Perry had foiled her plans with ease, but worse, far worse, was the knowledge that he now despised her as a heartless creature who had used his friend without compunction.

She could not blame him. She was deeply ashamed of her own behaviour, which had almost resulted in a duel between the two men. She'd never be able to lift her head again. She had destroyed their friendship without thinking of anyone but herself. Both young men must now regard her with disgust.

Poor Chris! He had looked so stricken. Elizabeth buried her face in her hands. She had been cruel to encourage him.

And Perry was still taking him to task. Even through the locked door she could hear his upraised voice as he demanded further explanations.

'Not here!' Chris said abruptly. 'You had best come to my cabin.'

Once there, he turned to face his companion.

'Save your recriminations, Perry. I knew what I was doing.'

'Did you? More to the point, did you know what Elizabeth was doing? Don't trouble to answer me. Your face gave you away. Admit it, you were shocked when you knew the truth of it.'

'I thought she loved me,' Chris said simply. 'Believe me, Perry, I didn't intend to help her to escape. How would she fare alone in a strange country? I wouldn't expose her to such dangers.'

'Certainly, I didn't think you capable of such folly... Damn it, man, she's played you like a fish on a hook.'

Chris coloured at that. 'It doesn't matter. I would still protect her with my life. I do love her, you know.'

'She isn't worth it.' Perry's voice was harsh, but he was moved to pity by his friend's misery. 'I don't mean to rip up at you,' he said more gently. 'You didn't know what she intended...but, if she can, she'll lead you by the nose.'

Chris managed a wan smile. 'She's very young. To her it's just a game. I did believe that she planned to play a trick on you to punish you for being cross with her. I didn't guess that she meant to leave me.'

Perry clapped him on the shoulder. 'Let it be a lesson to you. You won't be taken in again by that devious little brat.'

'I suppose not, but I wish you wouldn't speak of her like that. I pity her, in spite of all, cooped up in a cabin little bigger than a cupboard.'

'Like it or not, she'll stay there until we reach the shores of England. Cheer up! This ain't the end of the world, you know.'

Chris hesitated. 'Perry, you won't take it out on her? She don't see the dangers, so you mustn't come to points with her.'

Perry gave up. With a rueful shake of his head he returned to the quarterdeck. There, he found it impossible to concentrate on his duties.

He'd been expecting the attempt at escape, but not so soon. It had been a close-run thing. Had any other officer been on watch, Elizabeth might have slipped ashore.

Now he cursed himself for interfering. The chit had been trouble from the start. He should have turned a blind eye, and left her to face the consequences of her foolish act.

It would be bliss to be rid of her for ever. A high-spirited child? He thought not. When it came to womanly wiles, that little hornet had nothing in the world to learn.

Yet she'd been honest, and quick to intervene to prevent the inevitable outcome of that serious quarrel with Chris. When her chin went up, he'd known at once that she would tell the truth, exonerating Chris from any blame.

Pride alone had led her to confess, he thought with scorn. She would make no excuses. He was beginning to believe that she feared nothing and no one.

Well, he would show her who was master. From now on she would not take a breath without his knowledge. In a few weeks' time he would hand her over to her English relative.

His lips twitched at the thought of Miss Mary Grantham's probable reaction to her charge. Elizabeth was a handful, as that lady would soon discover, but it was no concern of his. With his duty to her father discharged, he could forget her.

He then remembered how her eyes had flashed when he had challenged her, and the way her delicate colour came and went. Strange, but even at the height of her fury the husky voice had lost nothing of its seductive charm. Another woman might have been screaming like a fishwife.

Later, he was surprised to find that his watch had passed so quickly. He went below to rouse Chris.

On the following day he was roused by the bustle on the docks. The provisioning of the *Artemis* was under way, and on the wharf alongside lay dozens of barrels of fresh water and puncheons of rum. Carcasses of pigs and goats were hauled aboard, and a number of smoked hams. Then came casks of flour and beef and butter, and crates of the necessary limes and lemons.

Most important was the vast quantity of powder and shot in various sizes, together with the matches, wads and priming-irons needed by the gunners.

Perry dressed quickly. It was clear that Captain Robsart hoped to sail without delay, but there was time to go ashore to make some hasty purchases.

He tapped at Elizabeth's door and then unlocked it to find her in a state of déshabillé.

'I beg your pardon,' he said hastily. 'Shall I go away?'

'What do you want?' Elizabeth asked coldly, as she reached for a dressing-robe.

'Ma'am, I am going ashore...' Perry was babbling, aware of nothing but the voluptuous beauty
the girl who stood before him. Her lace-trimmed

shift served only to emphasise the rounded curves of a creamy bosom, and a waist which was impossibly tiny.

Like many small-boned women, Elizabeth was not skinny. Clothed, she looked quite fragile, but now, clad only in her chemise, her firm curves were apparent.

Perry swallowed. 'Is there anything you need?'

'Nothing, I thank you,' came the brief reply. 'You cannot offer me fresh air, I think?'

'No, ma'am. I was thinking of some trifles for your comfort.'

'Those I shall leave to your discretion, Mr Wentworth. You hold my money. Use it as you think best.'

Perry longed to strike her, but turned on his heel and left. His offer had been made with the best of intentions. In return, she could only throw the money in his face. The woman was impossible. Was this to be the thanks he got when he offered only civility?

As he stepped to the ship's ladder, a midshipman, who had been about to remark on the fineness of the day, took one look at his grim face and thought better of it.

Perry soon recovered his spirits in the gentle warmth of the winter sun. As he strode through the main street of the port, he was greeted on all sides by officers of his acquaintance. Their banter cheered him, and it was in a more charitable frame of mind that he made his purchases.

The infuriating Miss Grantham must not be allowed to reduce him to her own level of petty spite.

Stepping into a small emporium, he bought a selection of sweetmeats, preserved fruits, and a jar of ginger in syrup. He added ratafia biscuits, and a box of fresh macaroons.

No gentleman carried his own parcels, so he ordered them to be sent to the ship.

Then, as he walked on, he spied a tiny chess set in a jeweller's window. The ivory pieces were intricately carved, and an enquiry confirmed that they were Oriental.

The set was expensive but, if it kept Elizabeth quiet for an hour or two, the cost would be well worth it. He didn't haggle, but paid the asking price, smiling ruefully at his strange behaviour. He didn't even know if she played the game, but she was intelligent and would soon learn.

He smiled again at the thought of teaching her. That would lead to some battles. It would not do to let her think that he had bought the thing. She'd probably throw it at his head.

He said as much to Chris.

'A peace-offering, Perry?' Chris examined the pieces with interest. 'It must have cost a fortune. She's sure to look more kindly on you.'

'She isn't to know that it came from me,' Perry said quickly. 'You must say that you asked me to look out for some such thing.'

'I can't do that. I won't be thanked for an expensive gift when I haven't paid for it.'

'Force yourself! Otherwise, she'll probably refuse to touch it.'

'That's true, but I wish you'd make your peace

with her. I don't mind telling you that all this quarrelling is a bore.'

'It isn't of my doing,' Perry pointed out. 'Still,
I'll try. Madam may simmer down if she gets a good
tossing in the Bay of Biscay.'

Chris grinned. 'You don't deceive me. You do
have some concern for her.' He gestured towards the
other purchases. 'What's all this? Briggs left them
at your cabin door, so I picked them up. More
games, old chap?'

'No!' Perry replied with dignity. 'Providing food
has been a problem. These are just some trifles to
help out.'

'Well, now, let's see. What have we here?' As
Chris examined the contents of the boxes he whistled. 'Just the things to keep body and soul together,
I'm sure! Such luxuries! They must have cost you
a month's pay. Am I to say that these, too, came
from me?'

'If you please.' Perry turned away to hide his embarrassment.

'But I don't please,' Chris told him frankly.
'However, since you will have it so… My stock with
the lady will certainly go up.'

Perry gave him a significant look. 'Just as long as
you don't allow her to persuade you into further
folly.'

'Oh, no, I shan't do that. I've learned my lesson.
She don't care for me, you know. Not in a loverly
way, I mean.'

'Don't let it worry you. It's my belief that she
don't care for anyone but this precious Count of
hers.'

'I'm not sure of that,' Chris told him thoughtfully.

'She don't talk about him much. She told me that she had mistaken her feelings for him.'

'She would, wouldn't she? Why would she promise to wed you if she still loved this cursed Italian?'

Chris looked uncomfortable. 'She didn't exactly promise,' he admitted. 'I suppose I hoped for it so much that I made myself believe it.'

Perry's face cleared. There was not the slightest reason why this piece of news should cheer him, but it did. 'I hope you ain't too disappointed,' he said more gently.

'I was, but I can understand it. Elizabeth won't give up without a fight. What would you have done?'

'I hope never to be brought aboard drugged, and in a basket.' Perry began to laugh. 'What would I have done? I don't know.'

'Exactly! I doubt if you'd have sat in a locked cabin twiddling your thumbs. You must give her credit for some spirit. I suppose that using me was all she could think of.'

Perry shook his head. 'Too generous by half, old chap! Will you never learn that she ain't to be trusted? Take her these things. If she thanks you, it's no more than you deserve. In your position I'd have longed to wring her neck.'

'I've never wanted to do that.' Chris chuckled. 'She's far too lovely...' With a sly look at Perry's face he went off with the parcels.

Elizabeth was standing by the port, gazing mournfully at the busy scene on the dockside. She was debating whether or not to call for help.

Might it not be better to risk the captain's wrath?

Most certainly she would be taken ashore at once, and delivered into the care of some British official.

Escape might then be just as difficult, but she would be spared the company of the obnoxious Mr Wentworth.

She opened her mouth to cry out. Then she closed it again, dismissing the notion from her mind. The obstacles might prove too great, she assured herself. Better the devil you know, and Peregrine Wentworth was a devil. He seemed to have an uncanny ability to read her mind, but she would defeat him yet. The urge to crush him outweighed all other considerations.

She spun round as the key turned in the lock, but it was Chris who came towards her.

'Good morning,' he said cheerfully. 'Here are some things for you. I hope you'll like them.'

'Are you heaping coals of fire upon my head?' she murmured in a low voice. She would not meet his eyes.

'Nothing of the sort! I expect I'd have done the same myself.'

'No, you wouldn't. You make me feel ashamed…'

'Stuff! Forget that nonsense! Ain't you going to open the parcels?'

As she made no move, he opened them himself, revealing the charming little chess set.

'Do you play?' he asked.

Elizabeth shook her head.

'No matter! I'll teach you.' He set out the foods upon the sea-chest.

Elizabeth gazed at him with a stricken face. 'I

can't accept these things,' she whispered. 'Oh, Chris, I have behaved so badly.'

'And now you plan to make things worse by spurning my offerings? That's a blow! I was hoping to help you eat the ginger. I have a passion for it.'

Elizabeth could not resist his teasing. She gave him a reluctant smile.

Chris patted her hand. 'We are still friends, are we not? Now, look at these ivory pieces! The carving is so intricate... The Chinese have talent for such things, or is it the Japanese? I forget.'

Elizabeth picked up one of the chessmen. 'The workmanship is very fine,' she agreed. Then she looked at him. 'Can you forgive me for the way I treated you?'

'It's all forgotten,' he assured her.

'So easily? What of Mr Wentworth. Is he still your friend? I was afraid. You came so close to a duel!'

'That happens twice a week,' he lied manfully. 'It don't mean a thing. Old Perry is quite over his ill temper. Can't think what's come over him. In the usual way he's full of fun.'

'I haven't found him so, but I expect that you understand him.'

'Not on this voyage, ma'am. Blest if he ain't been stamping about like a bear with a sore head.'

'I can't say that I blame him.' Elizabeth was determined to be fair. 'I'm afraid my father put him in a most difficult position, though he was acting with the best of intentions.'

'Perry knows that. He knows, too, that it ain't no fault of yours that you are here, but he feels a certain responsibility...'

'He need not do so,' Elizabeth replied with dignity. 'I am well able to take care of myself.'

'He don't see it that way. Besides, he can't understand why you don't wish to go to England. It's the finest country in the world, you know.'

Elizabeth smiled in spite of herself at the young man's earnest words. 'You would think so, naturally, but is it not always cold and grey, even in the summer?'

'Not always, ma'am. On a fine day the countryside is more beautiful than you could imagine.'

'Perhaps so, but you must remember that my family and my friends are all in Italy.'

'There is your aunt,' he ventured.

'A lady quite unknown to me.'

'But, Elizabeth, you will make friends. Think of your come out…the routs, the parties and the balls! Then you may attend the masquerades and the balloon ascents, aside from the military reviews.'

'My aunt may not agree to let me go.'

'She's sure to, ma'am. She won't ignore the Season.'

Elizabeth laughed. 'Aunt Mary has a certain reputation, sir. She makes no concessions to Polite Society.'

'She will wish you to be a success, and I am sure of it. You will have London at your feet.'

'Flatterer!' She smiled at him in disbelief. 'What shall I do with all London at my feet?'

'Step over the fortune-hunters, ma'am. There are enough about. Best beware of those April-squires, although I'm sure your aunt knows all about them.'

Elizabeth eyed him with affection. 'Will you always stand my friend?' she asked. 'I know I can rely on you.'

'And Perry too, Elizabeth. Oh, he may rip up at you, but beneath it all he's a splendid fellow. Forgive me if I speak frankly, but you have been at dagger-points since first you met. I told him that I didn't like it.'

'And what did Mr Wentworth say to that?'

'He's promised to mend his ways,' Chris told her with a grin.

The truth of his words was evident when Perry came to join them. The atmosphere of strained politeness was overwhelming. It was all too much for Chris.

'Have you two met before?' he demanded. 'What a stiff-necked pair you are. Perry, you ain't attending a funeral.'

Elizabeth began to smile, but Chris took her to task.

'You are just as bad, my dear. Why don't we start afresh? You might begin by calling Perry by his given name.'

Elizabeth hesitated, but she was not proof against his charm. 'Very well!' She looked up at Perry and held out her hand. 'The peace-maker shall have his way. Will you call me Elizabeth?'

As his hand enveloped hers she felt a strange sensation. It was as if some tingle of excitement passed between them...some message which she could not understand. Two pink spots of colour appeared upon her cheeks, and then she turned to pick up one of the chessmen.

'Have you seen these?' she murmured in confusion. 'They are very fine. Chris is to teach me how to play.'

Chris laughed. 'I did offer,' he admitted. 'But you'll do better with Perry. He's the expert.'

Perry dropped his air of dignity. 'That won't last for long,' he predicted. 'If Elizabeth's skill at cards is anything to go by, she'll soon be a master at chess.' He picked up the pack of cards. 'We've time for a game or two. What do you say?'

Elizabeth gave him her enchanting smile, and it caused him to drop the pieces of pasteboard.

'Clumsy!' Chris reproved. 'Pull yourself together, or this young lady will have both our fortunes...'

He was proved right. In the next hour Elizabeth trounced them soundly. Then the captain's bellow recalled both men to their duties.

Chris raised an eyebrow as he looked at Perry.

'We must be ahead of schedule,' Perry replied to the unasked question. 'We'll be under way by nightfall.' With a bow he excused himself.

Chris was quick to follow him, but before he left he pressed Elizabeth's hand. 'Don't worry!' he comforted. 'All will be well. I am convinced of it.'

It was with mixed emotions that Elizabeth heard the shouted orders, and the rattle of the chain as the anchor was raised. Then the great Rock faded into the darkness as they left the Straits and made for the open waters of the Atlantic.

Her last chance of escape had gone. Had she been foolish not to cry for help when they lay at berth in the docks? With each hour that passed she was being taken further from those that she held dear. She should have felt depressed. Instead, she was aware of a growing sense of excitement. Behind it lay another emotion which she did not care to examine too closely.

Chris had been so kind. How generous he had been in thinking of her comfort, in spite of her duplicity.

Idly, she nibbled at one of the preserved fruits as she thought of him with warm affection. He was a dear, and he'd looked so pleased when she and Perry had decided at last to call a truce.

Certainly, it was much more comfortable not to be always at dagger-drawing with that large young man.

When Perry laughed he looked quite charming, and behind those dancing eyes she had detected a wicked sense of humour. It had surprised her.

For some time she sat by the port, her book unopened on her knee, remembering his merry face, his teasing, and the way his blue eyes crinkled at the corners. When his lips parted they revealed white teeth, startling against the tanned skin.

The thought of that mobile, curving mouth was oddly disturbing, and a warm flush came unbidden to her cheeks.

She resolved to banish such thoughts. Peregrine Wentworth was still her enemy, and she must not forget it.

# Chapter Six

By next morning they were still within sight of land, though it was far distant.

'That is the coast of Portugal,' Chris replied in answer to her question. 'We should be safer now, with no chance of attack by pirates.'

'Pirates?' Elizabeth echoed blankly.

'Algerians. They put out from the African coast in search of single vessels, though they prefer merchantmen. The captain regards them as the scourge of the Mediterranean, though he don't like to fire on them. Their galleys are rowed by Christian slaves.'

'You mean that some of your own men may be their prisoners?' Elizabeth's eyes were wide with horror.

'There can be no doubt of it.'

'And women? Do they take them prisoner, too?'

'Yes, ma'am.'

'But women can't row the galleys. Are they held for ransom?'

'Not always.' Chris looked uncomfortable. He was saved from further explanation when Perry came to join them.

'What is it, Chris? You look as if you've just swallowed a frog.'

'I was telling Elizabeth about the Algerian pi-rates...' Chris was scarlet with embarrassment.

'And?'

'I was asking about the women prisoners,' Elizabeth explained.

'Are you sure you want to know?' The ironic note in Perry's voice wasn't lost on her.

'I think you might have warned me what I might expect if we were taken. Are they tortured?'

'You might call it that. They are stripped to reveal their charms, and sold in the marketplace at Algiers.'

Elizabeth paled. Then she made a valiant effort to recover her composure. 'To whom? Is this another jest? Admit it, you are trying to frighten me.'

'I shouldn't dream of it,' Perry told her solemnly. 'It would be a waste of time. Why, should you ob-ject to becoming a concubine in the harem of some sultan?'

'Perry, please!' Chris looked ready to sink with shame.

'It happens to be the truth. Now, do you see what might have been your fate if you had taken passage on a merchantman from Gibraltar to Genoa? That was your intention, was it not?'

Elizabeth's silence gave him his answer. Then she tried to justify herself.

'Do not the merchantmen travel in convoy, with a naval vessel to protect them?'

'Only when a warship can be spared. Besides, a single straggler offers chance enough.'

'You need not trouble your mind,' Chris said

soothingly. 'The Algerian galleys don't operate so far from their home ports.'

Elizabeth gave an audible sigh of relief. 'Where are we now?' she asked.

'Off the coast of Portugal. The Portuguese are our allies, so there is no danger of attack. It may be different when we reach the coast of France.'

Elizabeth nodded.

'Remember what I told you,' Perry continued. 'In case of an engagement I'll unlock this door, but you must stay here until we come to fetch you. Do you understand?'

She nodded again.

Perry threw open the lid of his sea-chest. 'You'll find some books in here,' he told her. 'My brother gave them to me. I haven't read them, but they may help to while away the journey. Help yourself.'

'I've already done so.' Elizabeth held up the book upon her lap. 'I thought you wouldn't mind.'

Chris eyed the title with alarm. 'Really, Perry! What can you be thinking of? *Tom Jones* is most unsuitable reading for a lady.'

Elizabeth stared at him. 'Why is that? I find it most exciting.' Then she surprised a twinkle in Perry's eyes, but he made no comment.

Chris continued his argument as they left the cabin.

'See here, Perry, that book is downright racy. There are some passages which are very near the bone...'

'She don't need to read them if they offend her. Elizabeth is no shrinking violet, but most probably she won't understand them, anyway. For God's sake, Chris! You take me to task when I ignore her,

and you ain't even satisfied when I try to help. Since
the book belongs to me, she'll probably lay it aside
in any case.'

He was mistaken. For the next few days Elizabeth
was fully absorbed in *The Adventures of Tom Jones*,
so much so that she found it difficult to lay the book
aside.

She had long grown accustomed to the sounds
aboard the *Artemis*. They were now so familiar that
she no longer heard the creaking of the mainmast,
or the winding of the cable round the capstan. Even
the cries of the gulls as they wheeled about the rigging didn't disturb her.

It was pleasant to take up her book and settle
herself in her chair, with only the slap of the waves
against the hull for company. She felt strangely at
peace with herself, forgetting her own troubles in
the company of Mr Fielding's engaging characters.

Early one morning that peace was rudely shattered when pandemonium broke out upon the deck
above her. She was aware of the sound of running
feet, and the barking of orders. Then there was a
rumble, and a loud report which almost deafened
her. It was followed by a fusillade of shot, and the
smell of powder reached her, even through the
locked door.

She jumped to her feet. They must be under attack. In great haste she threw a few of her possessions into the leather satchel. Then she ran to the
door, tugging at it wildly.

It gave at once, sending her staggering back. Then
Perry almost fell into the room.

'Gunnery practice!' he announced briefly. 'The crews compete against each other for accuracy and speed.'

'We are not under fire?'

'No!' He could see that she was trembling. 'Noisy, isn't it?' he murmured with a grin. 'Don't worry! I shall keep my promise. If we sight the enemy, you'll be the first to know. Were you frightened?'

'No!' she lied promptly. 'I was merely startled.'

Her brave words didn't deceive him. She was pale and shaking.

'It will soon be over. Powder and shot is expensive. We can't afford to waste it overmuch, but I must warn you. Tonight the guns will be run out again.'

'You can't fire at a target in the darkness,' she protested.

'We set fire to a cask or two, and get the men to row them out some distance from the side.' He laughed. 'We can't rely on the enemy only to attack in daylight.'

'I see.'

His words provided her with little comfort. She crushed a rising sense of panic. Somehow the thought of being on a sinking ship at night filled her with horror. To be cast adrift in an open boat on the wide wastes of the ocean was a terrifying prospect.

'The wind is rising, ma'am, and the seas are running high. This is the Bay of Biscay, and we may be in for a storm. In that case, you must lash yourself to something heavy...the side of the bunk, for example.'

'What with? I have nothing here.'

'I'll fetch you a length of rope in a while, and show you how to secure it.' He was as good as his word. Later, when the noise had died away, he returned.

'Are you sure that this is necessary?' Elizabeth eyed the length of rope.

'It's better than a broken limb, or a blow to the head if you should be thrown about the cabin.'

He tied the rope securely to the bunk, and then he turned to face her. 'Come here!' he said. 'If you leave this end attached, it will be easy to wind the rest about your waist like so...' Deftly, he spun her round until she was held fast. Then he smiled down at her.

That smile had a most disturbing effect upon her hard-won composure. He was much too close. She could see the small pulse beating in the hollow of his throat. Her own heart was thudding in such a way that he must be sure to hear it.

'I understand.' Thankfully, her voice was low and steady. 'Now, will you please untie me?'

'Must I?' he teased. 'Even without a storm I believe that you are safer so.'

Elizabeth glared at him. She would not beg for release. Instead she began to tug at the rope which held her.

Perry relented. 'Let me!' he said. As he unwound a coil or two the ship lurched suddenly, caught by a freak wave, and Elizabeth was thrown into his arms.

For a heart-stopping moment, Perry held her close, his face against her hair. Held against his heart, she felt like a small, trembling bird, vulnerable to his touch.

God, but he wanted her! The lovely body fitted
so perfectly against his own, united from thigh to
breast. He could smell the delicate fragrance of the
lavender water which he had bought for her, and
now the perfume was intoxicating, stealing imper-
ceptibly into every fibre of his being.

Elizabeth was taken by surprise. Too astonished
to struggle, she was conscious only of the strength
of the massive arms which held her.

She lifted her face to his with a question on her
lips, and then his mouth came down on hers. That
kiss was something new in her experience. No man
had ever used her so. When Cesare saluted her it
was with mere formality. She had permitted nothing
more than a chaste greeting, allowing him to kiss
her fingertips as convention demanded. He'd tried
to press her into further intimacies, but she had refused, unwilling to venture into a situation over
which she might have no control.

Now she had no choice. Perry had caught her unawares, and she found her senses reeling as his
warm flesh met her own. For a long moment the
world was lost. Then she heard a muttered excla-
mation, and his arms fell to his sides.

'Unforgivable!' he muttered hoarsely. 'Ma'am, I
had no right…I beg your pardon… This was the last
thing I intended.'

Elizabeth was badly shaken, but Perry was in
worse case. He sat down suddenly and put his head
in his hands. 'What must you think of me?' he
groaned. 'I have betrayed your father's trust.'

Elizabeth was struggling for composure. There
must be something she could do or say to make light

of the matter. He must never be allowed to know of
her delight in that lingering kiss.

'You are a sailor, sir. Are not naval men re-
nowned for their susceptibilities?'

Perry didn't reply. His expression told her that he
was disgusted by his own behaviour, and she felt a
strong desire to tease him. He had called her a hornet, had he not? Now, apparently, he had been stung.
She did not care. Her heart was singing. He had
proved beyond all doubt that he was not indifferent
to her.

Spurred on by some imp of mischief, she pretended to be scandalised, turning a deaf ear to his
renewed apologies. It was sweet to have him in her
power after the insults she had borne. Now she
would lead him a merry dance.

'Say no more!' she murmured in a crushed tone.
'This assault upon my virtue has quite undone
me...' Her voice was shaking, and she couldn't hide
the laughter in her eyes.

Perry glanced at her in deep suspicion. Then he
rose to his feet. 'I'm glad you find this so amusing,
madam,' he announced in icy tones. 'I might have
known that you would try to turn it to your own
advantage. You may rest assured that it won't happen again.'

'Come, sir, you make too much of a momentary
lapse.' Elizabeth could no longer keep her countenance. She looked at him with dancing eyes.

'Have you no sense at all?' he demanded harshly.
'An attack upon your virtue? What a child you are!
It was nothing of the sort, though it might well have
been. Had I not stopped myself in time, you would
not now be making game of me.'

Elizabeth knew that she had gone too far. His face was dark with anger, though it was directed more against himself than at her. For the first time she realised what might have happened. With his passions fully roused, Perry had almost lost control. It was chivalry alone which held him back. With another man she might not have been so lucky.

'Was it my fault?' she asked in a low voice.

'Of course not!' Perry ran impatient fingers through his dark locks. 'It wasn't anyone's fault, I suppose. As you say, it was a momentary lapse…simply an accident of nature. These things happen… Oh, Lord, Elizabeth, I beg you will forget that it ever did so.'

'It's forgotten!' she said simply. 'You did say that you had been at sea too long.'

That roused him from his misery. 'Not all naval men are rakes, whatever you may think.'

'You have not succeeded in convincing me of that.'

'Must you turn the knife in the wound? From now on, Chris alone shall keep you company.'

'You think him less susceptible to passion than yourself?'

'Susceptible? You have a low opinion of me, ma'am.'

'But I always had,' she murmured sweetly. 'Were you hoping that I might change it?'

'You may think what you will!' With the stiffest of bows he left her.

She now disliked him more than ever, and it was scarcely to be wondered at. He wasn't proud of his behaviour. In fact, he was furious with himself for giving way to that moment of temptation. To make advances to her was the last thing on his mind when he had entered the cabin.

It was just unfortunate that she had tumbled into his arms. After that, he had forgotten everything but her nearness, and the strength of his longing. He could remember now the surging joy as he held her close, and the beauty of that little flower-face as she lifted it to his. It was that which had finally undone his resolution.

He frowned and shook his head. He was making far too much of this matter of a single, stolen kiss, so there was little point in torturing himself.

Elizabeth herself thought nothing of it. She had made that clear. Even so, her reactions had surprised him. She had neither fainted, nor given way to strong hysterics. Indeed, she had melted into his arms as if to kiss him was the most natural thing in the world. And that moment had been sweet. Honesty forced him to admit it.

Of course, she was little more than a child, and quite without experience. God help the man she met when she realised her own powers.

A reluctant smile touched the corner of his mouth. What was it Chris had called her? A siren? The word described her perfectly. It would be as well to re-member that sirens were known to lead sailors to their doom.

A child she might be, but that kiss had roused emotions which were new to him. Behind the ur-gency he had been aware of a special tenderness, a longing to protect her. He shrugged. Doubtless at this moment she was making plans to escape from him as soon as they docked in England.

* * *

He was mistaken. Escape was not at the forefront of Elizabeth's mind at that moment. She was hugging her new-found knowledge to her. In that kiss, Perry had given himself away. Now she could better understand his constant rudeness, and his apparent dislike of her. He had been fighting his own feelings, unwilling to admit that he was strongly attracted to her. Perhaps he was afraid of an entanglement.

She had given him no encouragement. In fact, she could not remember ever behaving so badly in her life. She had sniped at him, insulted him, and done everything possible to make his life a misery. Her sense of wonder grew as she recalled the passionate insistence in his lips. In that embrace some spark had passed between them. She could not be mistaken, though it seemed impossible that he could ever grow to love her.

She thrust the thought aside. Perry was her enemy, and she must not forget it. It would not suit her plans at all to find herself in love with him. The idea was ridiculous.

She picked up her book again, but it did not hold her interest. She read the same lines several times, distracted by the memory of a pair of dark blue eyes, and the fascinating smile which made them crinkle at the corners.

She did not know how long she had been dreaming, but the growing darkness told her at last that it was time to light her lantern.

She heard a bustle on the deck, but this time it didn't startle her. When the guns went off she put her fingers to her ears to shut out the noise.

The training of the gun crews did not last for long. Then Chris came to join her.

'Released from your duties?' she asked with a friendly smile.

'Yes, ma'am. I brought your supper for you.'

'What is it?' Elizabeth sniffed appreciatively at the aroma from the steaming bowl.

'Kid stew. I told the cook that I was busy with my report, and would eat it in my cabin.'

'But I shall rob you of your dinner,' she protested.

'Hanley knows my appetite. He's given me enough for two.' With a look of triumph Chris produced another plate, and began to divide the meal. 'I've acquired a taste for goat...for kid, I mean...though I hadn't eaten it before I came to the Mediterranean. Try it! You'll find it very good.'

Elizabeth needed no persuasion, and they soon cleared their plates.

'You were not frightened by the guns?' Chris asked at last.

'No...Perry has explained. Are you pleased with the results of the practice?'

It was enough to set him off on a detailed explanation of the gunner's art.

'I wish you could see the men at work,' he told her. 'It's a splendid sight. The guns are rolled out and primed. Then the men stand by with lighted matches, waiting for the order to fire. The starboard crew won the prize this time. They blew the casks clear from the water.'

'It must be very different during an engagement with the enemy.'

'Of course. Then it is also a matter of good tactics and good seamanship. Captain Robsart is a master at the game. His tally of prizes is enormous, and he's sent many a vessel to the bottom.'

'But the men?' Elizabeth was distressed. 'You don't leave them to drown, I hope?'

'No, we fetch the prisoners aboard. Some are sent back to port with the prizes, in the charge of one of our officers. On the next occasion, I may be chosen.'

'Oh, I hope not!' she exclaimed. 'That would mean you leaving us. I confess that I should miss you.'

'Would you, Elizabeth?' His face grew rosy with pleasure. 'It may not happen. Perry is likely to be sent before me.'

'Oh, I had not thought of that.' Elizabeth said blankly. The possibility left her with a hollow feeling in the pit of her stomach.

'Don't worry! If he goes, you know that I'll take care of you. Besides, from here any prizes will be sailed to England.'

Elizabeth nodded. His words should have been a comfort, but they weren't.

Chris was determined to persevere. 'We've talked it over, Perry and I. If he should be injured, or carried off by a stray musket-ball, I'm to see you to your aunt.'

'Thank you!' she murmured in a faint voice. 'That is indeed a consolation.'

'Of course, it is unlikely.' A glance at her pale face warned Chris that he had said too much. 'Perry has more lives than a cat, though he does make a splendid target for the enemy snipers in the rigging. Up to now, he hasn't received a scratch.'

'I'm glad to hear it.' Elizabeth was trembling.

'Why, I could tell you of the times they've missed him by an inch—'

'Please don't!' She made an effort to change the subject. 'Won't you tell me about your family instead?'

She succeeded in diverting his attention, but when he left her she found herself a prey to hideous fancies.

Perry must not be killed or injured. She could not bear it. The thought of that fine body lying mangled on the deck was dreadful beyond belief. She bent her head, choking back the tears. What was happening to her? Why should she care?

The truth came to her slowly, and when it did, it shocked her. She could deceive herself no longer. She loved him, and to be without him would be merely to exist.

He must never be allowed to know, or he might be tempted to use her love against her. The small voice of her conscience asked if she had not planned to do the same. She ignored it, ashamed of her own weakness. Things had come to a pretty pass when a handsome face and figure could lead her thoughts so far astray as to make her wonder if to return to Italy was what she really wanted.

She wasn't thinking straight. She was tired…tired of living in this tiny cabin, tired of the degrading necessity of throwing her slops from the cabin window after dark, tired of monotonous food, and tired of being forced to wash in sea-water.

She pulled a face at her reflection in the mirror. Short though it was, her hair had lost its gleaming beauty. It felt unpleasantly limp, which wasn't surprising. It hadn't been dressed for weeks.

She had never washed her own hair in her life, but something must be done with it. Sea-water would not serve.

She said as much to Chris on the following day.

'I'll see what can be done,' he promised. 'Our fresh water is normally kept for drinking, and it is strictly rationed.'

'Then I'll save my ration until I have enough,' she told him.

When he mentioned it to Perry, that young man snorted in disgust.

'She has forgot. She doesn't have a ration. She ain't even supposed to be aboard. Of all the non-sensical ideas...'

'It isn't much to ask,' Chris murmured. 'She ain't complained of anything else, and ladies have these notions.'

'Bird-witted creatures, all of them!' Perry announced harshly.

Chris glanced at his face. The truce between Elizabeth and his friend seemed to be over. They must have quarrelled again.

'Elizabeth ain't bird-witted,' he objected. 'Perhaps if you explain about the water?'

'For God's sake, give it to her! Supplies ain't running low. She can have my share if she wants it.'

'Generous of you, old chap!' A suspicion was growing in Lord Christopher's mind. An old quotation came to him. It was just a thought, but it struck him forcibly. Did the gentleman protest too much?

'It ain't generous at all. I'd do anything to keep her quiet.' Perry's reply was unconvincing. 'See

what you can do. I shan't be much in her company
from now on.'

'Why not?'

'Too much to do!' Perry looked both unhappy and
bewildered as he went up to see the wheel relieved,
and to check their course.

Later, he returned to the same subject.

'Well?' he asked. 'Has madam washed her hair?
My God, as if it mattered! What will she think of
next?'

'She wouldn't take your ration.' Chris grinned at
him.

'She used her own? Now, I suppose, she is drinking wine.'

'It can't harm her,' Chris said mildly.

'You think not? She ain't used to it, for all she
says. Suppose she takes too much?'

'It would only make her drowsy.'

'Or ill. Before then she could take to singing, or
kicking up a rumpus. That would be all we need.'

'Perry, you sound like the village parson. If you
are so worried about her, why don't you tell her so?'

Perry turned away. His face was set, and Chris
realised that further argument would be useless. He
went on deck to arrange another gunnery practice.

In the event, it did not take place. With a heavy
sea running, it soon became too dangerous to handle
the guns. In the best of conditions they were a threat
to the crews who manned them. Once loosened from
their mounts and free to crash about the rolling deck,
they could cause more havoc than a dozen cannon-
balls. Deaths, or at best crushed limbs, were com-
monplace.

Within an hour they were struck by the full fury of a sudden storm. Elizabeth had listened with rising alarm to the sound of the wind as it screamed through the rigging like a soul in torment. From the port she could see only huge green walls of water as the *Artemis* sank deep into the trough of one wave after another.

The ship righted herself, only to fall like a stone once more, and Elizabeth lost her balance.

A pair of strong hands picked her up.

'Didn't I tell you to lash yourself down securely?' Perry demanded. 'You had best lie upon the bunk. We're in for some heavy weather.'

Before she could protest he laid her down, and threw the coverlet over her. The rope was quickly knotted about her person until she could not move.

Perry looked down at her, and then he smiled at the look of outrage on her face.

'You don't care to be trussed up like a turkey-cock? You'll thank me later, madam.' With this dark prediction he hurried away.

Elizabeth soon realised that he was right. The *Artemis* battled on bravely through the storm, but as the hours passed she became convinced that no vessel in the world was capable of surviving such a battering. Timbers creaked as the ship heeled over at a terrifying angle. Then she heard a crash. She closed her eyes, certain that they were about to founder.

By then she had decided that it no longer mattered. She felt so ill that she could only pray for a speedy end to her sufferings, yet the storm continued unabated.

At length, worn out by terror and exhaustion, she fell asleep.

When she awoke it was to find Perry by her side, busying himself with the ropes which held her. The *Artemis* was bobbing along like a gull upon the waves.

'Is it over?' she asked weakly.

'All over! We have sailed out of it.'

Elizabeth struggled to a sitting position. 'I was sure that we must go down…'

'It was just a blow,' Perry told her carelessly. 'Here, drink this!' He slipped an arm behind her and held a glass to her lips.

'What is it?' She eyed the glass with deep suspicion.

'It's brandy. You are used to it, of course?'

'Naturally!' With a defiant glare at him she swallowed rather more than she intended. It made her cough until the tears came to her eyes.

'Not your usual brand?' he murmured smoothly. 'My apologies, ma'am. We try to please, but our stocks are sadly limited.'

Elizabeth looked up with a sharp retort upon her lips, but his smile was so disarming that she left the words unspoken. Her heart began to pound. Would he kiss her again? Unconsciously, she nestled back into the hollow of his shoulder, unaware that she was putting temptation in his way.

Perry knew it. His self-control was being sorely tried. He withdrew his arm, rose to his feet, and held out the glass again.

'Won't you finish this?' he asked gently. 'You've had a shaking, and it will restore you… Later, you may wash your hair.' He gestured towards a small cask which he'd laid beside the sea-chest.

This was a peace-offering indeed. She smiled at him in gratitude, but then she hesitated, remembering Chris's words.

'Perhaps I shouldn't make use of the water,' she said doubtfully. 'It does seem selfish.'

'A few gallons won't make any difference,' he assured her, in direct contradiction to his previous strictures. 'Do you feel better now?'

She nodded.

'Then I'll leave you to your toilette.'

He was loath to go. She had courage, this one. Though the storm had been severe, she hadn't complained about her sufferings.

Unwilling admiration made him take her hand in his. He kissed her fingers in tribute, and left her.

It was a touching gesture, and her spirits rose. She walked over to the port to find the winter sun sparkling upon waves touched only by a slight breeze.

Then she shivered. The heavy weather must have driven them well to the north of the coast of Spain, and the temperature had fallen. She lifted out her warmest clothing, and set about the task of washing her short curls.

Not for the first time, she was glad that she'd insisted upon the latest 'Sappho' cut, in spite of her father's objections. As it was, the feathery tendrils were soon dry, and having regained their usual bounce, they clustered charmingly about her face.

That was better, she decided. Now she was ready to face the world, even though at present it consisted only of two young men.

She took up her book again, resolved to spend no

more time in thinking of her companions, but her good intentions failed her.

Chris was a dear, but it was Perry who filled her mind. He seemed to have forgotten his ill humour. Why had she ever imagined that Englishmen were lacking in kindness, charm or warmth? His smile alone was irresistible, and when he held her in his arms the world was lost.

She could not know it, but Perry too was deep in thought. In spite of all his resolutions not to do so, he had taken her in his arms again. This time the lapse was excusable. It was simply to help her to sit up. Even so, the brief contact had overwhelmed him with desire.

The urge to caress that milky skin, to kiss her neck, her eyelids, and to find her mouth again had been strong, but he had stopped himself in time, thank God!

It would not do. Elizabeth was beginning to occupy his mind to the exclusion of all else. It was a relief when Captain Robsart sent for him. Chris was already making his report.

'Well, gentlemen, are we ready for the enemy?' Captain Robsart wasted no time on pleasantries.

'We suffered only minor damage in the storm, sir. Repairs are well under way...' Perry hesitated.

'Yes, Mr Wentworth?'

'One of the men was injured when a gun broke loose. His foot was crushed to a pulp.'

'Next time he'll be sharper to jump clear.' Captain Robsart turned to Chris. 'The gun crews have improved, I see, and not before time. You may tell the men that their efforts are like to save their skins.'

Perry and Chris sighed with relief. This was the closest that the captain would come to admitting that he was pleased.

Now the crew of the *Artemis* had honed their skills to a peak of perfection. They had seen no sign of an enemy vessel, but that meant nothing. In these northern waters mist could lie low upon the sea, sometimes lifting to reveal a warship at close quarters.

When it came, the attack of the French frigate took them by surprise. She rose out of the mist like some legendary ghost ship, firing as she came.

# Chapter Seven

Elizabeth sprang to her feet at the sound of splintering timbers. Then she heard the cries of injured men. Was this another runaway gun? A second shot convinced her otherwise. The *Artemis* shuddered from the impact. They must be under attack.

Horrified, she rushed over to the port to find the frigate bearing down on them. It looked enormous. She could see the flashes and the clouds of smoke as the guns were fired in quick succession. The vessel was so close that she could see the features of the men perched in the rigging. Looking at their muskets, she guessed that these were the snipers, looking for a likely target.

Oh, where was Perry? He had promised to release her. Was he already lying injured? Sick with dread, she ran over to the door, tugging at it wildly. To her surprise it opened.

Either Perry had unlocked it earlier or the jamb had broken during the bombardment. She stepped outside and almost fell over the prone figure of a seaman at her feet.

The man was unrecognisable, his face a red mask

as blood flowed from a scalp wound. One of his legs was shattered from knee to ankle.

Elizabeth bent over him in time to catch a murmur.

'Help me!' he whispered. 'Can you get me to the surgeon?' His pain-filled eyes were pleading.

'I'll try.' Elizabeth forgot her own terror. 'Can you stand?'

'If you'll give me a hand...'

He was a brawny fellow, and it was only with the greatest difficulty that she managed to assist him to stand upon his one good leg.

'Lean on me!' she ordered. 'Which way now?'

'Straight ahead!' Dazed and half-unconscious, he showed no surprise to find her aboard the *Artemis*.

Their struggle down to the hold seemed to Elizabeth to take an eternity, and when they reached it she was exhausted. Then, as she looked about her, she forgot her aching limbs.

The scene might have come from Dante's *Inferno*. Wounded men lay everywhere, screaming, moaning, or lying ominously still. Sea-chests had been pushed together to make a rough operating-table, and in the dim light of the lanterns the surgeon was busy at his dreadful work.

Elizabeth waited until he had finished sewing up a long strip of tattered flesh.

'This man is badly injured,' she said briefly.

Startled, he looked up at her. 'What the devil?' Then he shrugged and turned his attention to the man beside her. 'Get him on here,' he said. 'Miss, this is no place for you. My assistant has been killed, and I have no time for fainting females.'

'I won't faint.' Elizabeth's chin went up. 'What can I do to help?'

A quick glance told him that she meant it. He gave her a hard stare. 'Most of them need water... others need cleaning up... And a prayer wouldn't come amiss.' With that he turned back to his grisly task. Elizabeth lost all track of time. She was dimly aware that the guns of the *Artemis* were firing without respite, and the din of battle was deafening, but she had no terrors now. All her attention was for the wounded.

One of the less seriously injured gave her a friendly grin. 'We're giving as good as we got, miss. That last shot from my gun took away their mainmast. The Frenchman is crippled now.'

She returned his smile, but she was only half-attending to his words. Others needed her more. Later, when the firing stopped, it made no difference to her. She was locked in a world of pain and death. She did not notice when the constant stream of wounded began to lessen.

It was as she bent over a rough pallet to comfort a man with hideous injuries that a harsh voice spoke above her head.

'Mr Wentworth, what is this? I gave orders that no women were to sail aboard this vessel...'

'Hush!' Elizabeth cried imperiously. 'Can't you see that this man is dying?'

Captain Robsart dropped to his knees beside her. There was no mistaking the livid hue of approaching death. Elizabeth ignored him, holding her patient's hand until the stertorous, irregular breathing stopped. With a last long sigh, the man expired, and she closed her eyes.

'Miss, you had best come with me,' the captain said more gently.

'Not now,' she muttered. 'I am needed here.' Elizabeth motioned him away. The man must be a fool if he thought she would desert the injured.

Captain Robsart was taken aback. On the *Artemis* his word was law, and he was unaccustomed to such cavalier dismissal of his wishes. He opened his mouth to order her obedience, but she had already moved away.

He stared at her in silence. There was something in her manner, perhaps in the carriage of her head, which told him that this was a lady of quality.

He drew his first lieutenant to one side. 'Mr Wentworth, I'll see you in my cabin.' He turned his back on Perry, and began to move among the wounded. Then, satisfied that the surgeon was doing all he could, he stamped away.

Perry followed him, dreading the coming interview. The shock of seeing Elizabeth in that hellish place of agony and death had unnerved him far beyond the fact that her presence had been discovered. He'd wanted to protect her. Instead, she'd been exposed to sights which a grown man would find difficult to endure. How was he to explain her presence to his superior officer?

The captain wasted no time. 'Well, sir, what have you to say? Will you tell me that the young lady is a stowaway? I hope not! I should not believe you.'

'No, sir. Miss Grantham is not a stowaway, though she was brought aboard without my knowledge... If I might explain?'

'Pray do so! You have my full attention!' The fierce eyes glared at his unfortunate subordinate.

In a few halting words, Perry tried to tell his story. Stated so baldly, it sounded too fantastic to be believed, but he struggled on, aware of the growing astonishment on the captain's face.

'You see, sir, by the time I found Miss Grantham we had sailed...it was too late to put her ashore...' His voice tailed away in misery.

He thought the captain would explode with rage. 'It did not occur to you to come to me?' he shouted. 'By God, sir, I won't have it! You conceal a passenger aboard this ship, and keep me in ignorance? She should have been put ashore in Gibraltar. Confess it, this is a cock-and-bull story, without a word of truth in it. She is your fancy-piece...'

Perry stiffened. He held his captain in a respect which bordered on awe, but the statement could not be allowed to pass.

'No, sir, she is not. I admit I feel responsible for her—'

'Do you, indeed? Then I wonder why you should see fit to expose her to the dangers of a voyage aboard a warship. What were you about, man, to allow her into that stinking hold?'

'I did not know of it,' Perry told him helplessly. 'She must have gone there on her own.'

'A likely tale!' The scorn in the captain's voice stung Perry to the quick. His face grew pale with anger. He would not be called a liar.

His voice was cold as he replied, 'Sir, it is the truth, I assure you.'

'I have no faith in your assurance. Fetch the young lady to me, and at once.'

Dismissed without ceremony, Perry made his way back to the hold. He took Elizabeth by the hand, and

tried to lead her away, but she resisted. Then the
surgeon came to her.

'You need rest,' he told her gently. 'You have
done all you can, and I don't want another patient
on my hands.'

Elizabeth looked doubtful.

'Go now!' he insisted. 'Madam, I am most grateful for your help. The men are in your debt. May I
know your name?'

'I am Elizabeth Grantham,' she replied in a weary
voice. Then Perry hurried her away.

'Where are you taking me?' she asked.

'Captain Robsart wishes to see you.' Perry sensed
that she was trembling with exhaustion, but he
would not release his grip upon her hand.

'But I can't...not like this. Just look at me!'
Elizabeth glanced down at her gown. The bodice
and the front of the skirt were stiff with drying
blood. 'You must let me change.'

'Forget it!' Perry told her grimly. 'We are in trouble enough. If we keep him waiting...'

'What can he do?' Elizabeth's chin went up. 'The
man isn't God, is he?'

'He's close enough aboard this vessel, so don't
fly into the boughs. I advise you to moderate your
tone.' He thrust her ahead of him at the captain's
command to enter the cabin.

Annoyed by the ferocious glare which greeted
her, Elizabeth stiffened and Perry closed his eyes,
fearing the worst.

'You may sit down, miss.' Captain Robsart was
quick to notice that she was close to collapse, in
spite of her air of hauteur. Only her grip upon the

back of a chair was holding her upright. He poured out a glass of wine and brought it to her.

'You must be very tired. Drink this! I should let you rest, but you must spare me a few minutes.'

Elizabeth nodded. She could not summon up the strength to argue.

'Now, madam, I will have the truth. Wentworth here has told me a story which I find hard to believe.'

'You may believe it, sir.' Elizabeth's eyes locked with his own. 'Mr Wentworth is not a liar.'

'But that your father would consider such a course of action...?'

'Here! This will prove it!' Elizabeth reached into her pocket, and thrust her father's letter into the captain's hand.

'I see!' The older man's face grew grave as he scanned the few paragraphs. 'Even so, Mr Wentworth, you have behaved very ill. I should break you here and now. You may go. Later, I shall consider further action.'

'You cannot mean to punish him?' Elizabeth cried hotly. 'That would be unjust!'

'Miss, you forget yourself...' The captain's eyebrows rose.

'No, I don't! I had heard that you were strict but fair. This is all my fault. I might have called for help...made myself known to you...'

'But you did not, Miss Grantham. Why was that?' His voice had grown more gentle. Her eager defence of Perry reminded him so forcibly of his youngest daughter, who was the darling of his heart.

'I don't know, sir...perhaps because I am not yet very wise...' Elizabeth had seen the change in his manner, and now she dimpled at him. That smile had caused many of her father's elderly friends to pinch her cheek, and accuse her of being a taking little minx.

The captain was no exception, and his stern face relaxed. 'Well, well, you are very young, I think. I could wish that you had not gone among the wounded. Such sights are most unsuitable for a lady.'

'I wanted to help,' she told him simply. 'Sir, will you excuse me? I should like to change my clothing.'

'Of course, of course! Thoughtless of me to keep you here in that condition. You have my thanks, you know, in spite of all. Wentworth, you and Miss Grantham will dine with me this evening.'

It was an order, rather than a request and, sensible of the honour done him, Perry bowed. Then he made haste to whisk Elizabeth from the captain's presence.

Outside the cabin, he heaved an audible sigh of relief. 'What a chance you took!' he murmured. 'Elizabeth, you must not speak to Captain Robsart in that high-and-mighty way. He is owed respect, you know.'

'Well, I do respect him,' she said artlessly. 'But I had to tell the truth. His bark is worse than his bite, I think. He is really quite a dear...'

Perry stared at her in stupefaction. Clearly, she was not intimidated by his formidable superior. He shook his head. Women were a race apart. He would never understand them.

This belief was confirmed later that evening as he, Elizabeth and Chris sat down to dine at the captain's table.

Cheered by the success of his brush with the enemy, Captain Robsart was in the best of spirits and Elizabeth encouraged this expansive mood. As he explained his use of various tactics to overcome the larger vessel, she hung upon his every word.

At length he paused, suddenly aware that details of a naval engagement were unlikely to be of much interest to his guest.

'Forgive me, I must be boring you, Miss Grantham.' To the astonishment of his junior officers he looked positively diffident.

'Not at all! I wish that I might have been on deck to see it.'

'That would never do, my dear. The snipers are the danger at close quarters. Sadly, it was a musket-ball which struck our purser.'

'Was that the man who died when I was with him? Had he any family...?'

'Aye! A wife and children, I believe. A bad business...I shall write to her, of course.'

He turned the conversation to more cheerful topics. 'Your father is a collector of antiquities, I believe. Do you share his interests?'

It was enough to divert Elizabeth's thoughts from the horrors of the day. Disclaiming any specialised knowledge, she began to chat about her father's treasures, ably assisted by Chris.

Perry alone was silent. He scarcely touched the turbot which was laid before them, and took only a mouthful of a fine ham braised in Madeira wine. Even a platter of cheese could not tempt him, and he waved away the tiny maids-of-honour.

The captain had not done with him, he knew that well enough. He had committed a serious breach of discipline, and his chosen career must now be at an end. It was a bitter pill to swallow.

And Chris? Was he to share the same fate? At all costs, he must be kept out of this unfortunate affair, but could the captain be brought to believe that he knew nothing of it?

Then Chris nudged him from beneath the table. Looking up, he saw Chris shake his head. It was a clear warning to pull himself together, but Captain Robsart had not noticed his preoccupation.

At that moment he was pressing Elizabeth to take another of the tiny cakes.

'We are not used to being so spoiled, Miss Grantham. Cook has sent them up for you.'

'They are delicious.' Elizabeth swallowed another mouthful, but the rigours of the day were beginning to take their toll.

Increasingly, she found it difficult to concentrate upon the conversation and at last she begged to be excused.

'Sleep well, Miss Grantham. You have my thanks, and that of all the crew. You have done well today.' With a courtly bow, the captain kissed her hand. Then he ordered Perry to see her to her cabin.

To her horror, she found that she was almost unable to stand. Swaying with weariness, she made no objection when Perry slipped an arm about her waist. Then he saw that her eyes were filled with tears.

'What is it, love?' he asked.

Elizabeth did not notice the endearment. Reaction was setting in. 'I was thinking of that man...the purser. How dreadful to die so far from those he loved.'

'Try to put it from your mind, Elizabeth. All sailors know the risks.'

'But it is such a waste…his poor wife, and his children…'

Perry threw open the cabin door. Then he kicked it closed behind him and took her in his arms.

'You are exhausted, dearest. Won't you try to rest? You did your best for him, and it must have been some comfort to him to have you there at the last.' He took out a snowy handkerchief and dabbed tenderly at her cheeks.

Elizabeth buried her face in his coat. 'It isn't much consolation. Am I being foolish? In the hold there was no time to think, but now it all comes back…'

Perry sat down and took her on his knee, rocking her like a child. 'You'll feel better tomorrow,' he promised. 'Things will be different since there is no longer any need for secrecy. You'll be much more comfortable.'

Still she clung to him, crushing his lapels. 'I don't care about that,' she choked out. 'Oh, Perry, will the captain punish you? I can't bear it!'

Gently, he disengaged her fingers. 'A first-class seaman like myself?' he joked. 'You can have no idea of all my skills. Where would Captain Robsart find such another paragon?'

'Are you teasing me again?' She gave him a misty smile.

'Of course not, goose! You've curbed his wrath, you little witch! He was purring like a pussy cat.'

'Did you think so?' She closed her eyes. Then her

head fell forward and, looking down, he realised that she had fallen fast asleep.

He shook her slightly, but he could not rouse her. With a sigh he laid her down upon the bunk, and began to untie the ribbons which secured her dainty sandals. Then he loosened the buttons of the gown which fastened to her throat. He could do no more.

Defenceless in sleep, she looked so vulnerable that his heart turned over. With a reverent hand he traced the line of one smooth cheek. What a mystery she was, lion-hearted one moment, and so feminine the next! He left the cabin quickly, before he was tempted into folly.

He returned to join Chris and the captain at their port, but when Chris rose to take his leave, Perry was requested to remain behind.

Were all his fears to be confirmed? He'd always loved the sea, and his naval career was all important to him. Now, as he waited to learn his fate, his heart was heavy.

Captain Robsart twirled the stem of his glass between his fingers. 'Well, Mr Wentworth, this is a pretty kettle of fish!'

Perry said nothing. He could not deny it.

'Miss Grantham is in a most difficult position. She has lived aboard this vessel, in your company, and without protection, for some time. Her reputation must now be in question!'

'Sir, I gave up my cabin to her. There has been nothing…I mean, she has not been harmed in any way.'

'Are you blind, young man? She is quite the loveliest woman I have ever seen. Who will believe that you have not made advances to her?'

Perry was about to protest his innocence. Then he remembered his fall from grace. He was unwilling to admit that he had kissed her, but his face gave him away.

'Quite!' the captain said drily. 'No man of flesh and blood could find her less than desirable. Now, sir, I believe you to be a man of honour. What do you suggest?'

'I...I don't know...' Perry stared at his superior officer.

'You disappoint me, Mr Wentworth. You know quite well that you must wed her.'

'Sir, with respect, I can't. I said as much to Mr Grantham when he suggested it.'

The fierce eyes regarded him with contempt. 'You have some previous commitment?'

'No, it is not that. I had no wish to be coerced. Besides, Elizabeth would never agree. She holds me in dislike.'

'Evidently a woman of some taste! However, that cannot be allowed to stand in the way of what is right and proper. In time you will learn to deal together...'

The captain hid a smile. He had his own views on Miss Grantham's opinion of his first lieutenant.

'There must be no delay,' he continued. 'Tomorrow you will speak to the young lady.'

Perry felt a sense of growing desperation. He could well imagine how the captain's orders would be received by Elizabeth. He withdrew in some disorder.

A sleepless night did nothing to ease his mind. On the following day he delayed his interview with

Elizabeth for as long as possible, but when he sought her out at last it was to find his cabin empty.

'Beg pardon, sir, but the captain sent his compliments to the young miss. She is taking breakfast with him.'

The smirk on the cabin boy's face vanished as he met Perry's stony gaze. He scurried away before the lieutenant's wrath could be visited on his head.

Perry groaned inwardly. Captain Robsart was not noted for his tact. It was entirely possible that he had already made his wishes clear to Elizabeth.

Perry winced. What an uproar that would cause. The girl would certainly refuse to marry him, and the captain would not tolerate open defiance.

He made his way to the captain's cabin, expecting to hear raised voices, but there was no answer to his knock.

'Miss is taking a turn about the deck,' a helpful crewman told him.

When Perry reached the quarterdeck, he realised that his initial fears were groundless. Elizabeth greeted him with a smile of unaffected pleasure, and the captain's expression was unclouded. In fact, he radiated benevolence.

'Captain Robsart has been telling me about his prize,' Elizabeth said eagerly. 'Did you know that she was carrying royalist prisoners?'

'Yes, ma'am.'

'Was that not a stroke of luck?' she continued. 'Now they are to sail the *Vainqueur* back to England when their mainmast is repaired. Captain, have I got that right?'

'Quite right, Miss Grantham. We shall make a

sailor of you yet. You are not too cold, I hope. You must not take a chill.'

'Oh, no!' Elizabeth snuggled deeper into her warm cloak. 'This is splendid! I love to feel the wind upon my face. How I envy you your life at sea!'

Perry glanced down at her. The fresh breeze had brought the colour to her cheeks and her eyes were shining.

'You still say that in spite of storm and warfare?' Captain Robsart teased her.

'No, not that!' she told him quickly. 'May I look in on the injured men today?'

'Later, if you please, my dear. I think you will not wish to attend the committal.'

'The committal? What is that?'

'The burial service, ma'am, when we commit the bodies of the dead to the deep.'

Elizabeth paled, but she turned to him with an air of resolution. 'I should like to join my prayers with yours,' she told him. 'How…how many died in the engagement?'

'Just two. We shall not lose more, I believe.' He frowned. 'Mr Wentworth, shall we be short-handed? I have been forced to send a prize-crew aboard the *Vainqueur*.'

'We shall manage, sir. Apart from Summers, who may lose a leg, most of the injuries were not serious. Many were caused by flying splinters.'

Elizabeth shuddered as she recalled the frightful wounds inflicted by dagger-like shafts of oak. As deadly as spears, they had flown across the deck, wreaking havoc among the men as they buried themselves deep in the flesh of some unfortunate victim.

'You think some of them are still able to bear a hand?'

'I believe so, sir. They are a hardy lot.' Perry looked at the lower deck, where the men already swarmed like ants. Under the direction of the ship's carpenter, order was taking the place of chaos as wreckage was tossed overboard, and the masts and rigging were restored to working order.

'Very good! Carry on, Mr Wentworth. I must prepare for the service.' With a brief smile for Elizabeth, the captain went below.

Perry was silent for some time, but his superior officer's instructions were not to be ignored. Yet he had no idea as to how to broach the subject to Elizabeth.

'You are quiet this morning,' she said at last. 'Is it because of this sad occasion?'

He did not reply to her question. Instead he asked another. 'Has the captain spoken to you?' he said bluntly.

'Of course!' Elizabeth looked astonished. 'He has been speaking to me for this hour and more.'

'Upon what subject?'

'He asked about my father, and my life at Genoa...' She gave him a puzzled look. 'Is that so strange?'

'Nothing more?'

She coloured a little. 'The captain likes to tease, I think. He wished to know if I had received many offers, and if I had a particular tendre for any of my suitors. Of course, I did not mention Cesare.'

'I see.' Perry hesitated. 'Forgive me, I have no

right to ask, but Chris mentioned that when he offered for you, you said that the Count no longer held first place in your affections. Is that true?'

'I did not lie to him!' Elizabeth's chin went up. 'Though I do not take it kindly that you have been discussing me.'

'How could we fail to do so?' Perry ignored the flash of anger in her eyes. 'You have not answered my question fully.'

'I did. I found that I had mistaken my feelings for Cesare. It was just a childish infatuation. I was very young when I first met him...'

'And now you are bowed down with age?' Perry's lips twitched.

She saw the smile, but to his surprise she didn't take offence. 'I think I have grown up a little,' she admitted sadly. 'Those injured men! My own concerns seem petty by comparison.'

At the sight of her troubled face, Perry longed to take her in his arms and comfort her, but he restrained himself.

'Elizabeth, will you listen carefully to what I have to say?' he asked.

She was struck by the grave note in his voice, and she turned to face him fully. 'What is it? Is something wrong?'

'Not exactly. At least, you may or may not think so when I tell you—'

'Go on! Don't keep me in suspense.'

Perry fixed his gaze upon the foaming wake of the ship. 'The thing is that Captain Robsart feels that you are in a difficult position. He pointed out to me that to travel alone, without a male relative to protect you, must necessarily cast a shadow upon your reputation—'

'I see!' Her voice had turned to ice. 'You explained, of course, that nothing untoward had taken place between us?'

'Didn't it?' Perry tried to take her hands in his, but she drew away. 'Have you forgotten that I kissed you?'

'A momentary impulse, sir, as you were careful to explain. I suppose you felt obliged to confess it to the captain?'

'No, I didn't!' His anger flared. 'What kind of a man do you think I am?'

'I have no idea, but I'm sure that you'll enlighten me. Pray let me know the worst. Am I to be cast adrift as a scarlet woman?'

'Now you are talking nonsense. The captain has your interests at heart, as you must know by now.'

'Then what does he suggest? Am I to dress in sackcloth and beat my breast while covering my head in ashes?'

'Try to curb your lively imagination, ma'am. He...er...he suggests that under the circumstances he should marry us.'

'What?' The word escaped her lips with such explosive force that the helmsman turned to stare. 'If you intend this as a tasteless joke...?'

'It is no joke, believe me. Captain Robsart thinks that it is what your father planned from the first.'

'That isn't true!' she cried hotly. 'He would have told me.'

'On the contrary, I'm afraid that it is true. He wished me to offer for you, but...' His voice tailed away.

'But you refused? Is that it? Why, sir, you surprise me! Just think, you have turned down an heiress!' Her look of contempt struck him like a physical blow.

'Don't!' he begged. 'Won't you hear me out? Elizabeth, we did not know each other. It would have been wrong of me to have agreed to a suggestion made in panic. You yourself would not have countenanced the idea.'

'In that, at least, you are right. Tell me, sir, what has changed your mind? You fear for your career? Is that it, if you disobey your captain's orders? I won't be sacrificed to your interests, Mr Wentworth.'

'It isn't that,' he told her doggedly. 'I had no thought of such matters.'

'I don't believe you,' she continued in the same hard tone. 'You have not exactly overwhelmed me with your passion. You must forgive me if I find myself lacking to the same degree. Shall you be flogged if I refuse you?' The martial light in her eye told him how much she welcomed the prospect.

'You don't understand,' he told her miserably.

'I think I do. As a naval officer, you must obey your captain, but I need not. Nothing in this world would persuade me to accept you, Mr Wentworth, and so I shall inform him.'

Elizabeth felt that she had tasted gall. Her bitterness threatened to overwhelm her. To be offered marriage merely as a sop to convention, and coming from a man who was acting under orders, was too insulting to be borne.

And it hurt the more because she loved him. She knew that now. Coming from another man, the

forced offer might have made her smile. She'd have
dismissed it without a second thought, but for Perry
to have made it? She felt wounded to the heart.

For a wild moment she found herself clutching at
straws. She could have accepted him, gone through
the marriage ceremony, and hoped that he would
grow to love her in the years to come.

She dismissed the thought. Always, in Perry's
mind, would be the feeling that he'd been coerced.
His offer was not made from choice, but from a
sense of duty. With that eating like a canker in his
soul, he might come to hate her. He did not care for
her. She could not delude herself. He had not spoken
a single word of love.

Her face flaming, she turned her back on him.
Then, as she looked down, the lower deck began to
fill with men. Half-dreading what was to come, but
determined to show her respect for the dead, she
went down to stand beside the captain.

Two shrouded figures lay on boards beside the
rail. Then the captain's firm voice read out the open-
ing words of the service used for burial at sea.

Elizabeth bent her head. It seemed all wrong that
the sun should still be shining on the sparkling sea,
and that the calls of the gulls could be heard so
clearly as they wheeled about the rigging. She
closed her eyes as the boards were tilted over the
side. With barely a splash, the weighted corpses vanished beneath the waves.

It was an awful sound. She found herself thinking
of the purser's wife and family, and the tears ran
unchecked down her cheeks.

'Come, my dear!' Captain Robsart took her arm,
and led her below.

# Chapter Eight

'A sad business, Miss Grantham!' Captain Robsart poured out a glass of brandy and offered it to Elizabeth, but she shook her head. 'These occasions affect even the roughest of the men.'

Elizabeth nodded, but she could not trust herself to speak, fearing that she might break down again.

'They know the risks of naval life, and they accept them,' he continued in an effort to comfort her. 'They would all appreciate your wish to attend the service.' He looked at her troubled face. 'Perhaps I should not have allowed it.'

'Captain, I'm glad you did,' she said simply. 'I wanted to pay my respects. It is just that I had no idea...until yesterday I had not seen the face of death.'

'But, Miss Grantham...yesterday...in the hold, you did not flinch...' The captain was amazed.

'There was no time to think about myself.'

He patted her hand. 'Well done!' he said. 'You are an example to us all.' He took a turn about the cabin. 'Even so, you cannot face the world alone. Has Wentworth spoken to you?'

'Yes, sir.' She did not pretend to misunderstand him.

'Then am I to wish you happy?'

Elizabeth shook her head.

'You will not tell me that you have refused him?'

'Sir, I cannot marry Mr Wentworth. We should not suit.'

'But why, my dear? He is of good family, and he has a fine career ahead of him. I am no judge of such matters, but I imagine that his appearance cannot be thought distasteful to a lady.'

Elizabeth made no reply.

'Perhaps he has offended you? I questioned him but he assures me that he has not attempted...I mean...that he has not made advances to you.'

'No, sir.' Elizabeth was scarlet with embarrassment. 'It is nothing like that.'

'What, then? Have you taken him in dislike? I'll admit that he has a deplorable tendency to levity, but that will pass with time. He is an excellent seaman, and I have great hopes of him. Before long, he will have his own command...'

Goaded into indiscretion, Elizabeth began to speak. 'I am sure that Mr Wentworth is everything you say, sir, but I shall not wed him. He offered for me at your order. How could he disobey you? Yet, I know that it was much against his wishes.'

Her face was a mask of anguish, and the captain cursed beneath his breath. His first lieutenant might be a splendid seaman, but where women were concerned he was a fool. Before the day was out, Mr Wentworth would feel the rough edge of his tongue.

He did not pursue the matter.

* * *

Later, however, when he sent for Perry, he did not mince his words.

'Well, sir, you have made a pretty mess of matters,' he snarled. 'Is this your idea of wooing? Tactics, bah! A child would have managed better.'

Perry's face was wooden. 'Sir, I don't understand...I told you that Miss Grantham would not have me.'

'And I'm not surprised! Great heavens, man, is it any wonder that she sent you to the right-about? What possessed you to tell her that you were acting under orders?'

'Captain, I had to explain to her the reason for my offer.'

'Lord give me strength!' Captain Robsart ran his fingers through his bristling crop. 'Sir, you are a blockhead! Had you no consideration for her feelings? Her pride? No woman of sensibility would take kindly to an offer made under duress.'

'I had to tell her the truth,' Perry said helplessly. 'She was surprised, you see, and when I mentioned your belief that it was what her father had intended, she didn't believe me.'

'You were unable to convince her?'

'I tried, sir. I told her that Mr Grantham had suggested it when we were in Genoa...'

'Pray don't keep me in suspense. What was your reply to him?'

'I refused, of course. I could not marry simply to oblige him.'

'And you explained this also to Miss Grantham?'

'I did, sir. I felt it only right—'

A bellow of rage prevented him from saying more.

'She should have hit you over the head with a belaying-pin! Get out, sir! You put me out of all patience with you.'

Perry turned to go.

'One moment, Mr Wentworth. For the rest of this voyage you will make yourself agreeable to the lady—that is, if she deigns to speak to you again. I won't have her upset. Do you understand me?'

'Perfectly, sir.' Perry was suffering from a sense of injury, but his face betrayed nothing of his feelings.

'And there is one more thing,' his captain continued. 'When we arrive at Portsmouth you will take extended leave. This is not an expression of my high regard for you. It is to enable you to see Miss Grantham into the care of her aunt.'

'Very good, sir.' Perry escaped at last. His collar felt uncomfortably tight, and he had the notion that it would have been preferable to be keelhauled, rather than to undergo the experience of the last few minutes.

He could not defend himself. The captain's voice had echoed his own feelings. What must Elizabeth think of him? No word of love, or even of affection, had passed his lips when he made that unfortunate offer. He couldn't believe that he had been such a dolt.

But it was too late now. In her eyes he must be sunk beneath reproach.

It shouldn't have mattered to him, but it did. He'd fought his feelings for her for so long, but now they wouldn't be denied. He'd learned to look for the determined little lifting of her chin, and the way emotions chased each other across the lovely flower-face. And her smile. Ah, that smile! It made his heart turn over in his breast. Now he remembered how it started in her eyes, and then those sweet lips curved...

His face grew grim. She would never smile at him in quite that way again, and the knowledge pierced his breast. He had lost both her friendship and her trust.

If only he might go back to the moment before he made his offer. He'd sensed a growing bond between them. The chess games, the cards, the teasing and the laughter had eased their enmity.

She was such a stalwart! He could not banish the memory of her small figure kneeling beside the dying purser, her skirt stiff with drying blood. The experience had taken its toll on her. He had guessed as much this morning, when she'd stood beside him at the burial service. He'd been convinced at one point that she was about to faint, but she had not done so, though there was naked agony in her eyes.

Perry straightened his shoulders. He would not lose her. He would regain her trust if it took a lifetime, and her affection, too. All he wanted was the chance to protect her, to banish that oddly vulnerable look which sometimes appeared when he'd caught her unawares.

If only he'd agreed to her father's suggestion, Elizabeth might now be his wife. The prospect brought a smile of tenderness to his lips.

Then he remembered. Elizabeth would have refused him. She must be won by subtler means. With a firm resolve to mend his ways, he went about his duties.

\* \* \*

He found the way back difficult at first. The constraint was evident between Elizabeth and himself.

Chris was moved to remonstrate. 'Next time I take a voyage for my health, I shall insist that my companions speak at least one word in the course of any hour,' he told them with a smile.

In unison they begged his pardon.

'What are your plans when we reach England?' Elizabeth asked.

'Family first, I think. My mother counts the days to my return.'

'And then?'

'London, and a visit to my Lords of the Admiralty. I hope to keep my name before them.'

'A wise plan,' Perry agreed. 'I intend to do the same.'

'You will visit London, then?' Elizabeth asked stiffly.

'Naturally, ma'am. I must escort you to your aunt.'

'More orders?' she murmured with a disdainful look.

Perry bowed. 'My pleasure entirely, ma'am.'

The irony was not lost on Chris. He glanced from one face to the other. Something had happened between these two, and on this occasion he felt powerless to mend matters. The rift was clearly deep and wounding.

'This aunt of yours?' he said. 'What do you know of her? You have not yet met her, so I understand.'

Elizabeth smiled up at him, grateful for his efforts to lighten the situation.

'Redoubtable!' she told him with a twinkle. 'That is the word my father uses to describe her. She is a spinster, and holds strong views, especially upon the male sex.'

'Oh, Lord!' Chris cowered in mock fright. 'I'd hoped to call upon you. Will she hint me away?'

'Of course not! How could she fail to like you? Besides, I shall be much in need of friends.'

'Then I may offer myself as escort?'

'To blue-stocking parties?' Elizabeth laughed. 'Shall you enjoy them, sir?'

'With you I shall,' he assured her. 'But you can't be serious. You mean that she attends these gatherings of hideous females, all bent on learned discussion?'

'They can't all be hideous,' Elizabeth said demurely.

'Nothing more certain,' he predicted. 'Sharp noses, teeth like tombstones, beady eyes, long, horsey faces... Oh, I beg your pardon! I did not mean your aunt, of course—' He stopped, conscious of his appalling lack of tact.

'Congratulations!' Perry said drily. 'Miss Grantham must be charmed by your opinion of her aunt, and that lady's friends.'

'Chris was only funning!' Elizabeth gave Perry a downing stare. 'I am not in the least offended.'

Perry subsided. It was clear that he was not to be forgiven.

'Oh, Lord! Are we back to formality again?' Chris pulled a comic face at his companions. 'What a pair you are! I thought we were to be on first-name terms.'

'That is up to Miss Grantham,' Perry told him stiffly.

'Well, have a heart, old chap! Is there any need

to look as if you've swallowed a poker? Damn it, Perry, if you ain't a mystery these days!'

Before he could demand an explanation, Elizabeth intervened. It was unfair to make him feel uncomfortable.

'Mr Wentworth...Perry...may be upon his high ropes, but I am not, I assure you, Chris. Won't you tell me more about the blue-stocking ladies? It is such an odd expression.'

'Never met one of them myself,' he assured her seriously. 'I hear that they wear blue silk stockings rather than the customary black to show their independence. When they meet they...er...jaw away, setting the world to rights.'

Elizabeth smiled at this bald explanation.

'Perry must know more about them,' Chris continued. 'His brother holds high office in the Government. What does Brandon say about them?'

Perry stole a sly glance at Elizabeth. This was a topic which was certain to divert her mind from his unfortunate proposal.

'Frederick thinks them misguided,' he announced solemnly. This was not strictly true, but he couldn't resist the temptation to tease Elizabeth. 'The matters they discuss are most unsuitable for ladies.'

As he had expected, her chin went up. 'Why is that?' she demanded. 'Does he fear that they will overthrow the Government?'

'It could happen,' he assured her. 'They hold strong political views. Generally, it is considered in certain circles that Mrs. Elizabeth Montagu has much to answer for!'

'What nonsense!' Elizabeth told him roundly. 'Are women not to think?'

'Most certainly! They may think of babies, of fashion, and even of gambling, to their hearts' content.'

Elizabeth's eyes flashed. 'How like a man to hold such views! We are not dolls, to be petted and patronised by men.'

Perry laughed, in spite of his determination to maintain his dignity. 'You think not? Allow me to inform you that the men who support the blue-stockings are considered traitors to their sex!'

Elizabeth saw the twinkle in his eyes, and realised that she was being baited. She was determined to hold her own in this discussion.

'Really? Such opposition must mean, then, that the blue-stockings are regarded as a threat to your present domination?'

Chris gave a shout of glee. 'Well done, Elizabeth! You have smitten him hip and thigh! Perry, admit it! You have been routed!'

'Not at all!' Perry found that he was enjoying himself. He was seized with the urge to lead her on. 'Will you tell me that you give no thought to bonnets, ribbons and muslins?'

'Of course I do!' she said uncertainly. 'But I think of other things, too.'

'Such as whether Denmark Lotion in the best restorative for the complexion?'

'Now you are gammoning me!' She gave him a reluctant smile.

'Not so, ma'am. We have not mentioned jewellery. That is a fancy not to be encouraged. It can prove expensive.'

'I must bow to your experience in such matters,' she told him wickedly.

Perry's shoulders began to shake. 'Have mercy, ma'am!' he begged. 'I am confounded! What can be more lowering to a man's esteem than to be in the company of a clever woman, especially when he ain't too bright himself?'

Her peal of laughter filled the cabin. 'You don't mean that. One cannot hold a conversation with a stupid person.'

'Ah, there you are mistaken! An inability to converse need be no drawback to a successful season, as long as the lady is presentable, biddable and an ornament to society. She must dance well, perform a little, perhaps upon the harp, which will show her to the best advantage, and be able to sing duets. Those, I believe, are the accomplishments considered necessary.'

'And are there many such paragons among the London *ton*?'

'Dozens!' he said ruefully. 'With not an idea between them.'

Elizabeth studied her fingers. 'I am surprised to find you still a bachelor,' she marvelled.

'Perry, that takes the trick!' Chris was convulsed with glee. 'Give it up! You won't best Elizabeth.'

She blushed a little at that. 'Well, it is all so foolish. Is a woman to have no opinions?'

'None!' Perry told her solemnly.

'Then I suppose I must resign myself to being shunned. I am inclined to speak my mind, you know.'

This artless statement was too much for her companions. They both went into whoops.

'You need not fall about like that,' she told them

with a kindling eye. 'I can't think what you find so amusing.'

'Beg pardon, ma'am!' Perry was the first to recover his composure. 'You sympathise with your namesake, then?'

'With Mrs Elizabeth Montagu? Of course I do! I shall attend these blue-stocking meetings with my aunt. Doubtless, I shall find them interesting.'

'Certainly!' Perry agreed in solemn tones. 'They are the answer for those wearied by the tedious amusements of society. One grows so bored with routs and balls, the visits to the sights of London, the balloon ascents, and riding in the Park. Nothing can be more dreary than a visit to the Vauxhall Gardens, or driving out to Richmond or Kew.'

Elizabeth eyed him with suspicion. 'I shall do all those things,' she promised. Then she saw the amusement on his face. It quite disarmed her, and she dimpled. 'Making may-game of me again?' she accused him.

When they parted Perry felt that he had gone some little way to restoring good relations with Elizabeth. Their discussion had been heated, but he sensed that she'd enjoyed it.

Even so, there was still a barrier between them. The memory of that unfortunate proposal and the reason for it could not be so easily forgotten.

Elizabeth herself was lost in thought. Up to now she had not considered what her life must be in London, but now it came forcibly to mind.

She began to wonder about her aunt. As a spinster, Miss Mary Grantham might find the charge of a young girl no pleasant prospect. It must, of necessity, force her to make changes to her way of life, and it would certainly disrupt her household.

Would she be the dragon that Elizabeth imagined? How often had her father shaken his head, dismayed by his sister's habit of travelling unattended to uncharted regions of the East. The dangers did not cross her mind, as Mr Grantham often pointed out.

And when she returned it was with the oddest notions. Was it not in Turkey that she had become convinced of the value of vaccination against smallpox? Elizabeth shuddered as she touched her own smooth cheek. For some, a frightful death from the disease was preferable to the ravages of a pockmarked skin. Many victims were forced to wear a mask, or to venture out only at night, when darkness hid them from horrified eyes.

She could not wonder that her aunt had sought some remedy against the scourge.

Her thoughts returned to Perry. Today he had been charming, and she had taken his teasing in good part. How she would miss the easy camaraderie of this voyage with himself and Chris.

However liberal her aunt's ideas, in London she would be forced to lead a more restricted life. The journey to England had been long, uncomfortable, and terrifying on more than one occasion, but she had no wish for it to end.

The reason was not far to seek. Perry's forced offer had wounded her to the heart, but she could not banish her love for him, though she had vowed to do so. Now, when their parting was growing ever nearer, she felt desolate.

She sighed. What a fool she was! He'd made his feelings about her all too clear. She had nothing in common with those feather-headed creatures he admired.

He did not care for her. That kiss which she had treasured might have been stolen from any tavern wench. Where was her pride? She had been rejected not once, but twice. At Genoa it was understandable. Her father's suggestion had come as a shock to him, but his unwilling obedience to his captain's orders had cut her to the quick.

A woman of any spirit would not have allowed herself to think of him at all. She longed for that blessed peace of mind, but it was impossible to achieve.

Once installed in London, all she could hope for was a formal meeting. That is, if he chose to call on her at all. Their conversation would be confined to platitudes.

But she must not fall prey to despair. Even if these last few weeks of close companionship had meant nothing to him, he could no longer think of her as a spoilt child. During the battle she had proved her worth in some small way, if only in her tending of the wounded.

How dared he offer for her at his captain's orders? Elizabeth's eyes flashed. The memory was still galling. An outright refusal to obey would have been far more to his credit. Nothing in his manner had suggested tenderness or affection. What a blow it would have been if she'd accepted him! A grim smile hovered about her lips. At this moment no doubt he was congratulating himself upon a narrow escape.

Her pride came to her rescue. She would not wear the willow for a man who didn't care for her. If her

life in London became unbearable, Aunt Grantham
might agree to send her back to Italy. That lady
might not share her father's fear of imminent invasion.

The thought should have cheered her, but it
didn't. She sighed and opened her book again.

Perry, too, was struggling with emotions which
were new to him. Under a full spread of canvas, the
*Artemis* was speeding home to Portsmouth in a fair
wind, and as he paced the quarterdeck he had plenty
of time for reflection.

Even more than Elizabeth, he was dreading landfall. At sea, he could be always in her company, but
he needed time to persuade her to think more kindly
of him. Not for the first time, he cursed his own
folly. So many opportunities had been wasted.

Once ashore, it would be far more difficult to persuade her of his love. Convention would make it
impossible for him to meet with her alone.

There would be the journey to London in her
company, but with the captain's notions of propriety
it was more than likely that he'd be saddled with
some genteel female to bear Elizabeth company. At
best he could expect an abigail to see to Elizabeth's
needs.

The notion brought an involuntary chuckle. He
could well imagine her reaction. An unknown female companion, genteel or otherwise, would not be
welcome to her. She had little use for the proprieties.

Blood will out, he told himself. From what little
he had learned about Miss Mary Grantham, it
seemed that she and Elizabeth were kindred spirits.

Both ladies were strong-minded, scorned convention, and had little regard for danger.

Yet he was not so foolish as to suppose that Miss Grantham's undoubted eccentricity would lead her into a damaging disregard for Elizabeth's reputation. The lady was no fool. His own brother held her in high regard. In Frederick's eyes, her brains did her no disservice.

Perry sighed. He might bid farewell to any hope of seeing Elizabeth every day, or dancing with her more than twice at any gathering. If she were allowed to drive with him, it would be under the supervision of a chaperon.

Why had he wasted all these weeks in bickering with his love? He should have had more sense. The time might have been better spent in wooing her, convincing her of his affection.

'Land ho!' A call from the crow's nest broke in upon his musings. The mist had lifted and to his right he saw the distant outline of the coast of France. By his reckoning the *Artemis* was off La Rochelle. By morning they would reach the English Channel. Unless the wind dropped, they would anchor in Portsmouth before nightfall.

Elizabeth, too, had heard the lookout's cry. Throwing her cloak about her shoulders she hurried on deck.

'Where are we?' she asked.

'We are off the French coast.'

'Shall we be attacked again?' she shivered.

'Don't be afraid!' Perry told her gently. 'An attack is unlikely. Their fleet is far to the south.'

Elizabeth drew herself to her full height. 'I'm not afraid!' she said with dignity. 'I'm shivering because

it is so very cold. The wind is like needles against
my face. How it cuts through clothing!'

'You will grow accustomed to our northern
weather,' he comforted. Then he smiled. 'We should
be lost without the vagaries of our climate. It is a
favourite topic of conversation...'

'Sir, you are teasing me again.'

'I assure you, it is quite true. Within a single day
we may have gales, rain, sunshine and even snow.'

'But only in the winter, I must hope.'

'I've known it to snow in May and June.'

'I don't believe you!' She was betrayed into a
gurgle of amusement.

'Just wait and see!'

'No, no! If it is as you say, I shall persuade my
aunt to send me back to Italy at once.'

'Is that what you wish for most?' Perry was looking down at her with an unfathomable expression.
Her eyes met his and then she looked away.

'Of course!' she lied. 'Can you doubt it? What is
there for me in England?'

Perry longed to tell her. At that moment he would
have offered her his heart, but her face was closed.

'You will find something,' he murmured lightly.

'Shall I? I wish that I could be so sure.' She left
him then and went below.


It was the rattle of the anchor-chain which wak-
ened her on the following morning. She ran to the
window to find the *Artemis* moored beside a bustling
quay.

This must be England. How quaint and foreign it
appeared to her curious eyes. She felt a little twinge
of panic, wondering how she would fare among this

nation of strangers. Then she heard a tapping at her door. It was Captain Robsart.

'My dear, you cannot travel on today. Will you do me the honour of staying at my home until arrangements can be made?'

Elizabeth thanked him with her prettiest smile. Perry was nowhere to be seen, so she gathered up her few possessions, bade farewell to Chris, and allowed herself to be led ashore and into a waiting carriage.

The captain's house was not far from the docks, and it was clear that his arrival was eagerly awaited.

As the carriage rolled to a halt two boys ran out to greet him, followed by a small, plump woman and a girl of about the same age as herself.

The captain kissed his wife. Then he chuckled as his daughter threw her arms about his neck.

'Tears, Carrie? I flattered myself that you'd be glad to see me.'

'Papa, of course I am, but you've been away so long…'

'Well, so I have, but now I am back again, and ready to keep you all in order.' The captain slipped an arm about his wife. 'I have brought you a visitor, my dear. This is Miss Grantham, come from Genoa. May I recommend her to your kindness?'

A pair of bright blue eyes examined Elizabeth. 'You sailed on the *Artemis*, Miss Grantham?' Clearly, the lady was astonished. She turned to her husband for an explanation.

'My love, it is a lengthy tale. Miss Grantham's father was concerned for her safety in these troubled times. Now she is to travel on to London to stay with her aunt.'

'I see.' The captain's wife was not altogether satisfied. 'Your woman, Miss Grantham? Does she follow with your baggage?'

'Ma'am, I came alone…without a maid, I mean…' Elizabeth flushed under the close scrutiny. For the first time she realised that it might not be so easy to avoid all suspicion of scandal. 'Please…if it is inconvenient for me to stay with you, I shall be happy to put up at an inn.'

Mrs Robsart looked at her again. The girl was obviously gently bred, and little older than her own Caroline.

'Nonsense!' she said briskly. 'That would not serve at all. You are most welcome here—that is, if you do not object to share with my daughter?'

Elizabeth curtsied. She felt uncomfortable, but she felt that she must accept. To insist upon staying at an inn alone would sink her even further in the eyes of the captain's wife. Even so, it was hateful to be here on sufferance.

Suddenly, she felt desperately homesick, and her lips quivered. She was perilously close to tears.

'There, there, my dear!' Mrs. Robsart laid a hand upon her arm. 'My bark is much worse than my bite, as my family will tell you. You must be very tired. Won't you go with Caroline?'

Elizabeth did as she was bidden, following the girl upstairs to a large and airy room furnished with two cots. She wondered why her companion did not speak. Then she realised that Caroline was too shy to address her.

'This is kind of you,' she murmured. 'Shall you mind sharing your room with me?'

'Oh, no, not at all!' Caroline blushed. 'Sometimes

I am allowed to have a friend to stay. It is so very lonely when Papa is away.'

'You must love him dearly.'

Caroline's shyness vanished. 'We all do!' she cried. 'He is the best father in the world.'

'Certainly, he has been very kind to me.'

'I'm so glad you like him,' Caroline said impulsively. 'Tell me about the voyage! When he is at sea I lie here wondering... Mama says that I allow my imagination to run away with me, but I can't help it. I picture him in danger...' Her eyes filled. 'You will think me very foolish, I expect.'

'No, I don't,' Elizabeth assured her warmly. 'But I think you have no need to worry. Captain Robsart is a splendid seaman. Why, when the French attacked, they stood no chance at all.'

Even as she uttered the words, she could have bitten out her tongue. What a thing to say! To admit that they had been in danger? She put out a hand to Caroline, but the girl's eyes were shining.

'He saved you all?'

'Indeed, he did! With the captain in command I was not afraid at all!' This wasn't strictly true, but the girl believed her.

'How brave you were!'

Elizabeth muttered a quick disclaimer. Then the arrival of her few possessions diverted Caroline's attention.

'My gowns are sadly crumpled, I'm afraid.' Elizabeth glanced at the creased garments in dismay. 'On board the *Artemis* I could not hang them up, or press them.'

'Jane will do that for you. She is the best of creatures.'

'Your mother's maid? I should not like to trouble her. At this moment I should like to throw them all away.'

'Miss Grantham, you can't mean it!' Caroline stroked the expensive fabric in appreciation. 'This cloth is so very fine, and look at the trimmings.'

Elizabeth smiled. 'Must you call me Miss Grantham? My name is Elizabeth. You think me extravagant, I fear, but if I am to go to London...?'

'Let us ask Mama. She will know what is best to be done.'

It was enough to set both girls chattering about the latest fashions.


In their absence the captain had put his wife in full possession of the facts relating to Elizabeth's situation. As he had expected, the story aroused both her sympathy and her indignation.

'Poor child!' she exclaimed. 'What was her father thinking of? To offer her hand in marriage to a total stranger, and then to bundle her aboard a ship, drugged as she was! My dear, I have no patience with such folly!'

'You don't quite understand, my love. I should not have done the same myself, but—'

'I should hope not, indeed! Suppose that this wicker basket had been cast into the hold? Miss Grantham might have starved to death, and no one any the wiser!'

'Her father took great care that it would not happen. His measures were extreme, I know, yet his fears for her safety were not unfounded.'

'Robsart, you put me out of patience!' his wife said roundly. 'A child is safer with its parents.'

'I wonder?' The captain puffed at his pipe. 'Europe may yet be set ablaze.'

'Well, I know nothing of these matters. I thank heaven that the girl was neither drowned, nor killed by a stray musket-ball.'

Her husband patted her hand. 'You are becoming as fanciful as Caroline,' he teased her.

'Am I? Next you will be telling me that you've just enjoyed a pleasure-cruise, and I, for one, will not believe you.'

He smiled at that, but he did not enlighten her.

'And how does your first lieutenant feel about all this?' she asked.

'Wentworth? I don't know. When I said that he must marry her, he did not care for the idea.'

'You *ordered* him to marry her?' Mrs. Robsart looked at him in blank amazement. 'Have your wits gone a-wandering, sir?'

'I meant it for the best,' the captain said defensively.

'No doubt!' Mrs. Robsart's tone was dry. 'What a matchmaker you are, to be sure! Between her father and yourself, that child must wonder if she is upon her head or her heels!'

'Well, you may judge the situation for yourself. If you have no objections, Wentworth will dine with us this evening.'

His wife gave him a sideways glance. Then she nodded, chuckling as she rose to drop a kiss upon his brow. The captain slipped an arm about her waist, and pulled her down to sit upon his knee.

'My dear sir, what are you about?' she protested laughing. 'Do you not hear the girls?'

Blushing with pleasure, she rose as Elizabeth came towards her, and was moved to kiss her cheek.

'Well, my dear, has Caroline made you comfortable?'

'She has, ma'am, and most kindly, but I beg that you will excuse my appearance. My clothing suffered somewhat on the voyage...'

'Jane shall press a gown for you to wear this evening, since Mr Wentworth is to dine with us.' She refrained from glancing at Elizabeth's face. Later, she would have time enough to judge how matters lay between this lovely girl, and her unwilling suitor.

# Chapter Nine

'I have asked Rainham too,' the captain murmured as an afterthought. 'Did I forget to mention that?'

'You did, my love.' Mrs Robsart threw her husband a look of mock reproach. 'I had best give orders in the kitchen.'

'Mama, before you go, Elizabeth would like your advice. She is to go to London, as you know, and she wondered...? She has so little clothing with her...'

'Let us speak of it later.' Mrs Robsart bustled away.

Caroline threw an arm about her father's neck.

'Looking for your present, puss?' he teased.

'Oh, no, Papa.' Caroline hung her head.

'Now, when did I return without some little trinket for you?' The captain reached into his pocket and produced a small flat leather case. 'Open it, my dear, before you die of curiosity.'

The case held a silver bracelet, ornamented with pearls and lapis lazuli.

'Blue stones...how beautiful. Papa, it will look so well with my new gown... Oh, thank you!'

'A new gown?' he said with mock severity. 'Have you been spending all my money while I was away?'

'I'd grown out of my others,' Caroline confided. 'They were bursting at the seams.'

'So now you are as fine as fivepence? Tonight, I see, I am to be dazzled.'

When the girls came down that evening, he professed to be struck dumb with admiration. His good humour was infectious and Elizabeth's spirits lifted.

Chris greeted her with his usual warmth, but she was aware only of Perry. She looked at his dark head as he bent to kiss her fingers, and her heart turned over. He looked magnificent. In honour of the occasion both men wore dress uniform, and his powerful frame showed off the blue coat laced with gold to full advantage.

She smiled a welcome, but he seemed unaware of it. His manner appeared to be intended to keep her at a distance—how she hated that air of stiff formality.

She turned away and addressed herself to Mrs Robsart. Her enquiry concerned the possibility of purchasing certain necessary items in the town next day, but she paid little attention to the reply.

Her hostess seemed unaware of the fact that two of her guests had lost their appetites. Yet she could have sworn that neither Perry nor Elizabeth knew what they were eating. The fish course was removed with barely a mouthful taken, and they made few inroads upon the mutton steaks with cucumber. Even a tart made with her finest preserved damsons

was left untouched. She was much too wise to press
them. Instead, she turned to Perry.

'How shall you travel to London, Mr Wentworth?
You have the choice of the Mail, or the stagecoach.'

'I thought of hiring a chaise, ma'am. It will be
quicker.'

Elizabeth's spirits sank. Did he wish to be rid of
her so soon?

'Do you think so?' Mrs Robsart asked. 'The roads
are so poor at this time of year, and we have had
heavy rains...' She did not voice her own belief that
to travel in a closed carriage with this personable
young man for so long a journey could only damage
Elizabeth's reputation, especially as she had no
woman with her. 'With the larger coaches there are
many willing hands to lift them from the ruts...' She
caught her husband's eye and subsided.

Perry had understood her perfectly. 'Perhaps you
know of some respectable woman who might accompany us? Elizabeth will need a maid.'

'An abigail?' Elizabeth glared at him. 'I have no
need—' She stopped, realising that she had spoken
out too sharply. She turned to her hostess with an
apologetic smile. 'I could not think of anything for
her to do, you see. I have few clothes.'

'You may find some things in Portsmouth,' Mrs
Robsart murmured calmly. This child had no idea
of the reason for her objection to the chaise. After
all, she had travelled for many weeks without a
chaperon. It was rather late in the day to be considering such matters. Until now she had come to no
harm, but she had seen nothing to assure her that
this desirable state of affairs would continue for
long.

Perry was deep in love, she was convinced of it, and she knew, too, that Elizabeth returned his affection.

At present, they were unaware of each other's feelings, but proximity was all. Men, in her experience, could be pushed just so far before their self-control snapped. Perry was no exception. It might take just a look, a gesture, an accidental touch, and they would be in each other's arms.

Later that night she voiced her fears to her husband.

'My love, you are mistaken,' he assured her. 'Wentworth does not care for her, else he would not have made such a shambles of the business. And Elizabeth gives him no encouragement. He told me himself that she holds him in dislike.'

'Sometimes I despair of you, my dear one!' With that his good lady slipped into bed beside him, and promptly forgot the star-crossed lovers in her own happiness.

On the following day she was relieved to find that Perry had taken her advice. He had booked two seats on the Mail coach which left Portsmouth early next morning.

'So soon?' she protested. 'We had hoped to keep Elizabeth with us at least until the end of the week.'

'You are very kind, but my aunt will be expecting me.' Elizabeth did not look at Perry. Her fears were confirmed. He could not wait to rid himself of his unwelcome charge.

It was with a heavy heart that she accompanied Caroline and Mrs Robsart into the town. There was no time to consider the buying of new garments, but it did not matter.

It didn't take her long to make her few small purchases, which consisted mainly of gloves, handkerchiefs and a bonnet. Jane had restored her wardrobe to something of its former glory, and she would not disgrace her aunt.

The household was up betimes next day to send her on her way with many expressions of goodwill. Elizabeth was touched. She'd known the captain's family for so short a time, yet they'd enveloped her in their warmth.

Now she had only Perry to remind her of those days aboard the *Artemis*, which already bore a dream-like quality. Had they really happened? It didn't seem possible now that she was seated in this crowded coach, her ankles grazed already by the basket of the woman opposite.

With a swift movement of his foot, Perry slid the basket further along, and she gave him a look of gratitude.

He didn't respond. His face remained impassive, and she felt a little spurt of anger. If he hadn't wished to accompany her to London, he should have said so. Much as she disliked the idea of a chaperon, the company of some respectable woman would have been preferable to that of a surly companion.

It wasn't true, and in her heart she knew it. These last few hours with him were precious to her. They were all she would have left to treasure, even though he was here against his will.

She could not know the true state of his feelings. At that moment all he desired in life was to hand

Elizabeth into a closed chaise, and set off in search
of the nearest parson.

He groaned inwardly. Such a course would do his
cause no good at all. Desperate though he was, to
kidnap Elizabeth now would turn her dislike into
hatred. In an elopement, the bride must be willing.
He could imagine her reply if she were asked at the
ceremony to take him for her husband. It would be
a sharp refusal.

He stole a sideways glance at her. Stiff and cold
in manner, she was sitting bolt upright, and her expression didn't encourage conversation. He could
see only her profile as she gazed out at the winter
landscape.

It was no bleaker than her thoughts, but she refused to give way to despair. In time, Aunt Mary
might be persuaded to send her back to Italy, away
from this hard grey land where the men were as cold
as ice.

'I beg your pardon, ma'am?' Elizabeth found that
she was being addressed by the woman with the
basket.

'I asked if you go all the way to London, miss?'

'Why, yes! Forgive me, I am still half-asleep. We
made such an early start...'

'A weary journey!' The man beside her shook his
head. 'I have no faith that we shall reach our destination without mishap.'

'You fear that we may be stopped by highway-
men?' Elizabeth was startled by his dire prediction.

'No, no! There is no danger. The guard is armed.'

The woman with the basket paled. 'And doubtless
drunk, together with the driver—'

'At this hour of the day?' Perry was quick to intervene. 'I saw no sign of it.'

'Wait until we stop, my dear sir! They will make full use of the taproom, and the coachman has but one eye. His lead horse, too, is blind. I am convinced of it... They will overturn us, mark my words.'

Elizabeth found it difficult to keep her countenance. Beside her she felt Perry's shoulders shaking. It was too much for her. She tried to turn her laughter into a cough, and promptly choked.

Their lugubrious companion brightened. He launched into a discourse upon the evils of travelling in the winter months, and the number of his friends who had been carried off by a variety of diseases, including an inflammation of the lungs.

Elizabeth was soon helpless, and was forced to bury her face in her handkerchief.


At their first stop, Perry hurried her away from the others.

'You are a disgrace!' he grinned. 'Next thing the driver will be asked to put us off.'

'I'm sorry!' she said weakly. 'I couldn't help it. Do you blame me?'

'No, I don't.' His own eyes were dancing. 'Dear God! What a Jeremiah!'

'I'll do better when we go on,' she promised him. 'That is, if he doesn't start again...' This sent her off into a fresh peal.

'How good it is to see you laugh like that!' Perry told her warmly. 'I could almost forgive that miserable creature. When we set out you looked so sad.'

'I was thinking...well...'

'Yes?' he asked eagerly. A faint hope stirred

within his breast. Could it be that she would miss him?

'Oh, nothing! I am being foolish. It is this weather. The rain and the mist have sunk my spirits and it is so very cold.'

'You need a hot drink,' he murmured. 'Buttered rum, I think.'

Elizabeth was doubtful, but when the steaming potion appeared she drank it gratefully. As the strong spirit coursed through her veins, even her toes began to tingle.

'Better?' Perry was laughing down at her.

'Much better! This is very good, but it tastes rather strong.'

'It is!' Perry was unrepentant. 'It may send you to sleep, but I'll wake you if you snore.'

'I don't snore.' Elizabeth was indignant.

'How do you know? You can't listen to yourself. Still, it isn't wise to drink on an empty stomach, or you may decide to entertain us with a song or two on the rest of the journey.' A snap of his fingers brought the landlord to his side, and he ordered ham and eggs, a dish to which he and Elizabeth did full justice.

In the event, it was their dismal companion who had imbibed too freely at the inn. He was soon sound asleep.

The farmer in the opposite corner nodded towards the recumbent figure. 'There's one who thrives on prophecies of disaster,' he chuckled as he addressed himself to Perry. 'I fancy that you, sir, do not share his fears?'

Perry laughed and shook his head.

'I thought not. Have you seen much action, captain?'

'My dear sir, I am not a captain, merely a first lieutenant, lately returned from the Mediterranean Sea.'

'Were you engaged with the French?'

'We were, but I'm glad to say that we came off best.' Perry smiled at Elizabeth, remembering their shared danger.

'Murdering critturs!' The woman with the basket snorted in disgust. 'When I think of their poor Queen! What's to become of her little ones?'

'I don't know, ma'am. At this present time I hear they are imprisoned.'

'It's a disgrace! Mad dogs, the lot of them... It's as well, sir, that we have you to keep us safe, but your poor little wife here must be fair sick with worry.'

'She keeps up well, ma'am. It isn't the French who worry her...rather it is the mermaids...'

His listeners laughed heartily at the joke, and Elizabeth joined in.

'No, no, I won't have mermaids!' she exclaimed. 'That is coming it too brown.'

She'd been about to correct the woman's mistake, but then she decided that it would be less embarrassing to ignore it, rather than to embark upon an explanation.

Perry laid his hand upon his heart. 'Do you doubt me? How can that be when I always tell the truth?'

Her expression changed. He was not referring to the wonders of the deep and she knew it. With a grave face she turned away.

* * *

When they stopped again there was no time for conversation. The fog had delayed them and the coachman was anxious to push on.

'Well, I must have my tea,' the woman with the basket told him. 'And it is too hot to drink.'

'I can't help that, ma'am. I must keep to my schedule.'

'We'll see about that,' the woman whispered to Elizabeth. Whilst the driver's back was turned, she tossed the teaspoons into the pot, and immediately started a hue and cry for them. In the resulting up-roar she was able to enjoy her tea at leisure.

Finally she emptied the teapot and turned to the landlord in surprise.

'Why, sir, I believe your spoons are here! Sheer carelessness, I call it! You must keep a closer eye upon your kitchen-maids.' She was moved to accept his apologies with good grace, but the coachman eyed her with suspicion.

The woman ignored him as she took her seat once more. She winked at Elizabeth. 'Surly crittur! That will teach him a lesson!'

Elizabeth smiled, but she was feeling desperately weary. She closed her eyes and slept for several hours.

When she awoke it was to find herself nestling comfortably within the shelter of Perry's encircling arm. He was gazing down at her with an expression of such tenderness that her heart turned over. Her enchanting smile peeped out as he bent towards her, but it was merely to tell her that they had almost reached their destination.

He seemed about to say more, but the other travellers were awake, and the opportunity was lost.

In the darkness she could see little of her surroundings, but as they rattled on through the streets of London she realised that the city was much larger than she had supposed. Suddenly she was afraid. In a short time now she must leave the protection of the man she loved to face this alien world alone.

Perry sensed her feelings, but there was little he could do to comfort her. It was not until they had been set down, and he'd hired a passing jarvey that they found themselves alone.

'Don't worry!' he murmured gently. 'Now you will be safe.'

When she turned to him her smile was tremulous. She longed to tell him that she had no wish to be safe in the company of her aunt. Her lips quivered as she fought the urge to beg him not to leave her.

'Don't look like that, Elizabeth! All will be well, I promise you.' It was only with a supreme effort that he stopped himself from taking her in his arms and covering her face with kisses. Yet he knew that he must not speak now, when she was so vulnerable.

He would do his best to win her, but if she ever agreed to wed him, it must be because she loved him, rather than because she was afraid of the unknown.

When they drew up at the house in Mount Street, he handed her down from the carriage, and turned to pay the driver. Elizabeth stood motionless beside him.

Then, much against his will, he guided her lagging footsteps to the door. The knocker had not been removed, so the owner must be in residence. He reached out and sounded a loud tattoo.

There was a lengthy silence. Then he knocked again and they heard the sound of shuffling foot-steps.

The door opened to reveal an ancient individual who gave them a look of mute enquiry.

'We are here to see Miss Mary Grantham,' Perry said firmly.

'Who shall I say is calling, sir?'

'Miss Grantham...Miss Elizabeth Grantham. She is come to visit her aunt.'

The porter gave them a look of consternation. 'I don't know, sir, I'm sure. Madam said that she was not to be disturbed under any circumstances. She ain't at home to anyone.'

'She must be at home to her own niece.' Perry shouldered his way inside, drawing Elizabeth with him. 'You will announce this lady, if you please.'

'She ain't expected,' the old man said stubbornly.

'Do as I say!' Perry roared. His voice had shaken the timbers of the *Artemis* on many an occasion, and now it sent the porter shuffling away, muttering to himself.

The wait for his return seemed interminable, but he was back at last.

'You are to come with me,' he mumbled.

Elizabeth hung back, tugging at Perry's sleeve. 'I shouldn't have come,' she whispered. 'My father's letter cannot have arrived.'

Perry smiled down at her. 'Courage!' he said softly. 'Let us meet the lady.' He took her arm and urged her on across the hall.

When they stopped outside the heavy oaken door

the voice which bade them enter was clear, deep and authoritative.

Elizabeth found herself in a room notable only for its disarray. Books lined the walls and lay in piles upon the floor, beside a number of pictures stacked in rows. Dust lay so thick upon the furniture that she might have written her name in it.

She had no time to look about her further.

'Come here!' the imperious voice demanded.

Elizabeth made her way to the far end of the room. Then she stopped, arrested by the odd appearance of her aunt.

Clad in the fashion of some fifty years earlier, Miss Grantham wore a sacklike garment, apparently made of linen, over her hooped skirt. A woollen cap was perched at an angle upon her powdered wig, and her hands were hidden by thick mittens.

Thin to the point of emaciation, her eyes were her most outstanding feature. Huge and brilliant, they sparkled with intelligence as she bent them full upon her niece.

'Well, miss, you won't get lost,' she announced at last. 'You are the image of your mother. Is my brother with you?'

'He is still in Genoa, ma'am.'

'Not sick, I hope.'

'No, Aunt.'

'Then why are you here without him? And who is this young man? Have you eloped?'

'Certainly not!' Elizabeth cried warmly. She introduced Perry, and started upon a halting explanation.

Miss Grantham heard her out, with only an occasional snort of disgust.

'I won't say I'm surprised,' she said at length. 'My brother never had much sense.'

'You shan't say that!' Elizabeth was stung into making a sharp reply. 'He thought that he was acting for the best.'

'Hoity-toity, miss! Is that what you have learned in Italy…no respect for your elders?'

'Not if they speak unjustly.' Elizabeth's face grew pink with anger.

'Hmm! Well, I suppose that I must take you in.'

It was not the warmest of welcomes, and Elizabeth was about to beg her not to trouble herself, when a look from Perry stopped her.

'I think you know my brother, ma'am,' he murmured pleasantly.

'Heavens, the creature has a tongue! Wentworth, you say? Are you related to the Earl of Brandon?'

'Yes, ma'am. He is my eldest brother.'

'Does he know that he has a gapeseed for a relative?'

'He assures me of it constantly.' Perry grinned at the formidable old lady.

'Quite right! He ain't altogether a fool. I know Sebastian better. How does he go on?'

'He is well, Miss Grantham. Prudence has just given him a second son.'

'Your mother must be pleased. A sensible woman! I can't think what queer fancy keeps her always in the country. You may tell her that I'd like to see her if she comes to town.'

Perry bowed and twinkled at her. 'You are very kind, ma'am.'

'No, I ain't. Don't think it! Well, sir, this is a pretty kettle of fish, as I'm sure you will agree.'

Perry sensed her anxiety as her eyes rested upon Elizabeth.

'You are thought to be…er…redoubtable, Miss Grantham. Your brother is convinced of it.' His eyes were dancing wickedly.

'None of your sauce, young man!' She gave him a reluctant smile. 'Well, Elizabeth, have you also lost your tongue?'

Elizabeth was not attending to the conversation. Her eyes were fixed in horrified fascination upon a row of glass jars, neatly arranged upon a shelf, in which were visible certain parts of the human anatomy, preserved in spirits of wine.

The old lady chortled. 'Squeamish, miss? You don't care to understand the workings of your body?'

'No, ma'am, it is not that. I was surprised…I did not expect…'

'If that's the only surprise you get in life, you will be fortunate. Pray don't cast up your accounts in here. If you feel faint, put your head between your knees.'

'Elizabeth won't faint, ma'am.' Perry made haste to intervene. 'She ain't squeamish in the least. If you had seen her with the wounded, you would not think it.'

'You were attacked?' Miss Grantham motioned to her companions to sit down, making way for them by sweeping piles of papers off two chairs.

'I'm working on a treatise,' she explained. 'Now, sir, pray continue. Tell me what happened.'

As Perry began to speak, her gaze roved from one face to the other. 'Elizabeth', was it, then? The undue familiarity failed to shock her, but it gave her

pause for thought. Her niece was clearly a girl of
spirit, though she seemed oddly downcast.

And Wentworth? Though he answered all her
questions readily, she sensed that his thoughts were
far away.

It did not take her long to decide the true state of
affairs. She waited until Perry had finished his tale.

'And what now, sir?' she asked. 'Do you return
at once to Portsmouth?'

'No, ma'am. I have been granted extended leave.'

'I see. Your captain was happy to be rid of you?
Was that it?'

'That…and the fact that the *Artemis* must undergo
repairs.' Perry's smile had lost none of its charm.
'Mainly, it is because Captain Robsart wished me to
see Elizabeth delivered safely into your care.'

'Well, you have done so. Shall you go into Kent
to see your family?'

'I think so, ma'am. I have been away for many
months. I may return to London to see Frederick.'

Miss Grantham hid a smile. It would not be the
urge to visit his brother which would bring this personable young man back to London. In some amusement, she awaited his next words.

'I wondered if I might call upon you, ma'am?'

'Most certainly, my dear sir. You have some particular interest in our movement?'

'The blue-stockings? Good Lord, no!' Caught unawares, Perry was betrayed into speaking his mind
aloud. It was a gaffe of some magnitude, but he
made a quick recovery, though his face was scarlet.
'I beg your pardon. I should not have mentioned
your movement in such terms.'

'Why not? If we don't take exception to the label,

why should you?' Her face betrayed grim satisfaction at having teased him into an indiscretion. 'Yes, you may call upon us, sir. We shall welcome a new member at our meetings, and, who knows, you may learn something.'

The look of dismay upon his face was nothing short of ludicrous, and Miss Grantham's composure was sorely tried. She hadn't enjoyed herself so much for years. Now she waited to see how he would extricate himself from a situation which obviously filled him with dread.

'I hoped that you might allow me to take Elizabeth driving in Hyde Park, and take her about to see the sights,' he suggested.

'Did you, indeed! That won't be possible, Mr Wentworth. That is, unless some understanding exists already between you...?' As she expected, this remark brought an instant response from her companions.

'No!' they cried in unison. The sharp reaction confirmed her earlier suspicions. These two were deeply in love, though neither would admit it to the other.

Must she play fairy godmother to these foolish children? The notion diverted her, but when she spoke again her face betrayed nothing of her feelings.

'We have my niece's reputation to consider,' she murmured.

Elizabeth tossed her head. 'I don't care for that!'

'Then, my girl, you are a fool! To be shunned by society will not make you feel more comfortable, and shunned you will be if you are thought to be fast. That would *not* please your father.'

'Of course not!' Perry was quick to accept the inevitable. 'But, ma'am, if you cared to drive with us...?'

He avoided Elizabeth's eyes, well aware that she despised him for his cowardly acquiescence.

'You flatter me, sir!' Miss Grantham's tone was heavy with irony. 'We shall see! You have done your part, and I must thank you for it.' She held out her hand to him.

It was a clear indication of dismissal, and he had no alternative but to accept it. He bowed, and then was gone.

'Handsome creature, ain't he?' Miss Grantham said slyly.

'Who? Oh, you mean Wentworth? I suppose so. I hadn't given it much thought...'

This outrageous fib tempted Miss Grantham to enquire if her niece had been afflicted by a sudden attack of blindness but she changed the subject.

'Come, we must find a room for you,' she announced briskly. 'Where are your things?'

Elizabeth pointed to the small portmanteau by her side.

'I see. Then you have little more than you stand up in? That is easily remedied. I don't care much for fal-lals, but if you are to make your come-out...'

'I don't wish to make my come-out,' Elizabeth cried in despair. 'Aunt, won't you send me back to Genoa?'

'Certainly not!'

'But why? You think my father over-anxious for my safety, and you can't wish to have me here. I thought you despised society...'

A grim laugh preceded the reply. 'I can afford to

do so. You cannot. You have your life before you, and now you have the choice. You may make it as pleasant or as miserable as you wish.' She looked at her niece's downcast face. 'What *do* you wish, my dear?'

She had a shrewd idea, but if she'd hoped for a confession of Elizabeth's love for Perry she was to be disappointed.

'I don't know.' Elizabeth turned away. 'Freedom, I suppose, and the opportunity to lead my own life. Now you tell me that I may not do so. Aunt, I was told that you did not care for the proprieties.'

'My dear child, I am very old, and also very rich. A wealthy woman may be allowed her eccentricities. A large sum invested in the Funds doesn't incur disapproval from any source.'

This forthright and cynical statement brought an unwilling smile to Elizabeth's lips.

'I could do the same,' she suggested.

'Perhaps…in sixty years' time!' Without more ado she led the way across the hall, and up the ornate staircase. 'Shall you be comfortable in here?'

Elizabeth looked about her. Even in the light of a single candelabra, the room was awe-inspiring. Not only was it huge, but the massive furniture cast shadows everywhere. It was also very cold.

Miss Grantham tugged at the bell-rope. 'Bessie will light your fire,' she said. 'I expect you'd like to take your supper here this evening. Ring for anything you need. I'll leave you now.' With that she closed the door behind her.

Elizabeth pulled her cloak about her. She sat down in a wing-chair, shivering uncontrollably, and a prey to a dozen nameless fears.

She felt bereft. Perry should not have left her with this strange, brusque woman for whom she could never learn to feel the least affection. It was hard to believe that Aunt Grantham was related to her gentle father. She missed him quite dreadfully. That could be the only reason why she felt so close to tears. It was not because of Perry. He had walked away without a second glance.

She swallowed hastily as she heard a tapping at her door.

'Madam said that I was to light your fire, miss.' The girl who entered carried a warming-pan, which she thrust into the bed. Then she struck a light from her tinderbox, and set the sticks ablaze.

'My, but it's dark in here.' With a generous disregard for the cost of beeswax candles, she moved about the room with a taper, until the soft glow of a dozen candles banished the ominous shadows. 'Must I unpack your bag?'

'Thank you. You are Bessie, are you not?'

The girl curtsied. It didn't take her long to dispose of Elizabeth's few possessions. Then she excused herself.

'I'll fetch your supper, ma'am. It will help to warm you up.' Her grin was infectious. 'I'm sorry it's so cold, but this room ain't used much.'

Her friendly manner did much to raise Elizabeth's spirits. When she returned, it was with a tray containing chicken broth, some sliced cold beef, a salad, and some fruit.

'This is a lot of trouble for you,' Elizabeth said shyly.

'No trouble, ma'am, and Cook is ever so pleased.

Miss Grantham don't eat enough to keep a bird alive…'

Elizabeth looked at the tray. The broth smelled delicious and suddenly she felt very hungry. With a promise to return in time to help her to retire, Bessie whisked away.

Elizabeth did full justice to the meal, but by the time she finished, she was feeling drowsy. Grateful for the warmth of the blazing fire, she dozed until the maid returned.

'Well, now, didn't I tell Cook that you'd have a good appetite, Miss Elizabeth? Now she'll be able to make up some of her special dishes for you.' Bessie cast a critical eye upon the visitor. 'You look ready for your bed, miss. Let me help you with your gown.'

Gratefully, Elizabeth submitted to her ministrations. Tucked into the warmth of the enormous bed, she smiled up at Bessie. She hadn't felt so comfortable since the day she left her father's house.

# Chapter Ten

It was many hours before Miss Grantham followed Elizabeth's example. In the sanctuary of her study she considered the problem now before her.

The child was a taking little thing, and she had spirit, but how would they deal together?

She herself was much too wily a bird to change her own brusque manner. She despised emotional blackmail. Her niece must take her as she was. Neither old age nor loneliness must be used as tools to win Elizabeth's affection.

Upon one thing she was resolved. The girl must not be allowed to return to Italy. In Elizabeth's presence she had laughed her brother's fears to scorn, but they could not be dismissed so lightly.

Would she herself have stayed in London, braving the rigours of an English winter, were it not for the present situation? Soon all Europe might be ablaze. She was no coward, but neither was she reckless.

And did Elizabeth really wish to leave? If Peregrine Wentworth should return to London all might yet be well. She grimaced. Now she was matchmaking. It was another female habit she despised.

Her lips twisted in a smile of pure self-mockery. It was one thing to cherish high-minded notions as to the correct behaviour of the human race. It was quite another to put them into practice. Shaking her head at her own folly, she retired to bed.


On the following morning Elizabeth joined her aunt in the dining-room upon the stroke of nine. Such punctuality brought a nod of approval from her aunt.

'You are no slug-a-bed, I see. Now, miss, I will hear more of your story. You did not tell me all, I think.'

'Ma'am?'

'Elizabeth, I am no fool! You will not tell me that you managed to avoid discovery during your voyage on the *Artemis*?'

'I did until we were attacked. Then the captain saw me with the wounded.'

'And what had he to say?'

Elizabeth flushed. 'He was scandalised,' she admitted. 'It was so foolish! There was nothing untoward. Perry had given up his cabin to me...' She fell silent.

'Then why are you so angry? Wentworth must have given an explanation.'

'It wasn't good enough for Captain Robsart. He said...he said that Perry ought to marry me.'

'Naturally you refused?' Miss Grantham murmured smoothly. She was beginning to understand much which had previously been a mystery to her.

'Of course I did! Perry was forced to offer for me

when he had no wish to do so, as he had already told my father. I wouldn't accept him if he were the last man in the world, though, of course, he won't offer again, now that he is under no coercion.' This happy state of affairs appeared to offer Elizabeth no satisfaction.

'Very wise, my dear!' Miss Grantham nodded sagely. 'Nothing could be more lowering to a woman of sensibility than to be rejected twice. Doubtless, Wentworth refused because of a previous commitment.'

'No, he didn't!' Elizabeth's eyes flashed. 'He refused because he doesn't like me. The women he admires are weak, and mealy-mouthed, with no opinions worth discussing. He told me so himself.'

'Extraordinary! I thank heaven that it cannot matter to you. You don't even think him handsome! These days so many girls are dazzled by a uniform, a pair of broad shoulders, and a certain type of charm. I'm glad to know that you are not among them.'

Elizabeth looked up sharply, but her aunt's expression was bland.

'Looks are not everything!' Elizabeth snapped.

'Of course not! Now, my dear, today I hold a small soirée. You will wish to meet my friends. Then we must see what can be done to clothe you for the coming Season.'

Elizabeth smiled politely. She had not the least desire to attend the soirée, but common courtesy prevented her from saying so. As for the Season…with any luck she would be far from here before it began in April.

Her aunt chuckled. 'I am no fashion-plate myself,

as you will have noticed, but Lady Mountfield is to visit us today. Her daughter is an elegant creature, and most amiable. We shall persuade her to advise us.'

'Ma'am, I cannot think it necessary,' Elizabeth protested. 'I shall not go about so very much.'

'Nonsense! Is not Wentworth to take you driving in the Park?'

'But I thought you said…?'

'I've changed my mind. Had your head been filled with romantical notions about him I should not have considered it. Under the circumstances, it can do no harm. My groom may go with you.'

'I doubt if we shall see him again,' Elizabeth predicted in gloomy tones.

'Possibly not, but it was civil of him to offer. We must grant him that at least.'

'I expect he feels that he owes some duty to my father,' Elizabeth told her bitterly. 'Though why he should, I can't imagine.'

'Don't trouble your head about it. If we women tried to understand the workings of men's minds, we should think of nothing else. Now, my dear, will you occupy yourself this morning? I have much to do.'

Dismissed until lunchtime, Elizabeth returned to her room. Bessie had carried off her gowns to press them, and returned with a pile of snowy underthings which she had laundered on the previous evening.

A glance at Elizabeth's face told her that the girl was low in spirits.

'Shall I wash your hair, miss?' she suggested. 'It's lost its curl, and the ends are sticking out.'

Elizabeth was forced to smile. It was evident that

Miss Grantham did not choose her servants for their tact.

'What a good idea!' she agreed. 'I confess that it was a trial when we were at sea. I suppose it was the salt air.'

Bessie wasted no time in fetching up hot water. 'Cook will send up something for you when we've finished,' she announced. 'Miss Grantham don't trouble to eat a nuncheon.'

Elizabeth allowed herself to be led over to the washstand. It was bliss to feel Bessie's strong fingers on her scalp and, when she finally emerged from beneath an enveloping towel, she felt much refreshed.

Her short crop was soon dry. The dark curls clustered about her face in a shining glory, framing her brilliant eyes.

'My, but you're a beauty!' Bessie was lost in admiration. 'You'll be the toast of London.'

Elizabeth laughed. 'What shall I wear for this soirée?' she asked. 'I don't wish to disgrace my aunt.'

'Lord bless you, Miss Elizabeth! It don't matter! Wait until you see the ladies! There ain't a soul among them as gives a thought to what they wear. It's my belief that they throws on whatever comes to hand.'

Later, Elizabeth was forced to admit that she was right. In her own plain gown of fine India muslin, embroidered only at the hem, she felt almost inconspicuous among the old-fashioned hoops, the feathers, and the amazing turbans favoured by her aunt's intellectual friends.

She guessed correctly that none among them

could lay claim to less than seventy years, and that included the gentlemen.

Elizabeth was no stranger to social skills. Well accustomed to the ponderous gallantry of her father's friends, she moved through the gathering, blushing at compliments, and listening with charming deference to the ladies.

Miss Grantham was well pleased. She was prepared to give credit where it was due, and Elizabeth's manners were a tribute to her upbringing.

She rapped upon a table and called her guests to order. For the next hour they listened to a learned dissertation upon the uses of herbal medicines. It was well researched, but Elizabeth found her attention wandering.

Where was Perry now? Doubtless he was entertaining his family with the story of his unwelcome charge. She pressed her hands to her burning cheeks. They would find it most amusing.

She was recalled to the present when her aunt rang for refreshments. The wine was excellent and plentiful, and it was accompanied by delicious little patties, cheeses, chicken wings, and various sweetmeats. Miss Grantham might not care for food, but she did not stint her guests.

It was as Elizabeth was repelling the advances of an elderly gentleman, somewhat the worse for wine, that the door of the salon opened. She looked up to see Perry standing in the doorway.

Elizabeth's heart turned over. In full dress uniform he looked magnificent. Resplendent in his coat of blue and gold, his black stock neatly tied, he towered above the gathering, his white waistcoat and breeches dazzling in their snowy perfection.

There was a moment of silence. Then a *frisson* of excitement ran around the room. Miss Grantham looked at the members of her learned circle in astonishment. The stupid creatures were twittering like schoolgirls, straightening their shawls, and patting ineffectually at their greying curls.

She held out her hand to Perry. 'Well, sir, do you now hold the record for the journey into Kent and back?'

'Ma'am, I didn't go.' Perry looked a little conscious. 'I called upon my brother, Frederick. Prudence and Sebastian are staying with him, and my mother too...'

'I see. You felt obliged to hurry here to inform me of this fact?'

'Well, I...er...you expressed a wish to see my mother, ma'am.'

'So I did!' Her eyes were twinkling. 'Allow me to present you to my guests.'

'Miss Grantham, I must beg your pardon. I have no wish to intrude upon your party—'

'Nonsense! You are welcome. Such a pity that you didn't arrive an hour ago! We've had a most interesting talk upon the uses of herbs.'

'Good Lord! Is that what you were doing?' Perry stopped. 'I mean...well, of course, it must have been fascinating...'

'It was!' Miss Grantham laughed aloud. 'Come, sir, the ladies wish to meet you.'

This, she felt, was an understatement. Perry was the lion of the hour, and was treated as such.

His charm was evident as he replied with endless

patience to questions about his family and his naval service. He even managed to parry more searching questions from several of the more outspoken ladies.

Elizabeth smiled. Blue-stockings they might be, but they weren't above indulging in a little gossip.

Miss Grantham watched him from the corner of her eye. To her relief he didn't single out Elizabeth, greeting her only with the formal courtesy which he might offer to any lady of his acquaintance.

Elizabeth, too, had kept her countenance. Her face was composed as she gave him her hand, only her heightened colour betraying her inner turmoil.

Such behaviour deserved its own reward, and as her guests were leaving, Miss Grantham signalled to Perry to remain. Then she dismissed Elizabeth to her bed.

She sat down by the fire, and motioned Perry into the opposite chair.

'Now, sir, you may tell me why you are here.'

'Ma'am, I hoped you might relent. Frederick has offered me the use of his perch-phaeton, and if you will consent, I'd like to drive Elizabeth in the Park tomorrow.'

Miss Grantham studied her fingers. 'Let us have pound-dealing,' she said at last. 'What are your intentions towards my niece?'

'You must have guessed them, Miss Grantham. I love Elizabeth and I want to marry her, but she will have none of it.'

'Are you surprised?'

'No, I'm not!' he told her bluntly. 'I've been an idiot, ma'am. I made a mess of the whole business.'

'I fear you did. Was it necessary to mention that pressure had been brought to bear upon you twice?'

'I wanted to be honest with her.'

'An admirable notion, but not always the best policy. There is such a thing as tact...'

'I know that now.' Perry ran his fingers through his hair. 'Miss Grantham, is there any hope for me? She don't trust me. If I offer for her again, she's sure to think that it is out of pity. She don't wish to be here, you see. She has no friends in England.'

Miss Grantham let this unfortunate comment pass. Tact was never likely to be Perry's strong point.

'You are right,' she told him. 'You must not offer again just yet. Once trust is lost...'

'I'll try to regain it,' he cried eagerly. 'Won't you help me, ma'am? I love Elizabeth with all my heart...'

'I cannot do your wooing for you, sir. I am no meddler, and I won't interfere.'

'No! I would not ask it of you, but I wondered if you knew? She has said nothing to you?'

Miss Grantham shook her head.

'Then you have no idea of how she feels?'

'None whatever!' the old lady lied. Perry must not know that Elizabeth had already lost her heart to him. He must find out for himself. She looked at his bent head.

'Mr Wentworth, you may call tomorrow. You may take Elizabeth driving. My groom will accompany you.'

Perry's head went up. 'Thank you!' he said with feeling.

'And let me give you some advice. You will not expose my niece to gossip, sir, nor will you worry her with your advances.'

Perry seized her hand and kissed it. 'Of course not! I know I must go slowly.'

'Well, I wish you luck! Now be off with you, you rogue! It is long past my bedtime.'

This was not true. Miss Grantham needed little sleep. She was accustomed to read and write long into the night, but on this occasion she found it impossible to do either. She frowned. To be playing Cupid at her age was nonsensical. She was behaving no better than the matchmakers she despised so much.

Yet this was not a question of selling Elizabeth to the highest bidder. The girl was an heiress in her own right, but Miss Grantham had become convinced that it did not weigh with Perry. She doubted if it had ever crossed his mind. His love was deep and true, and she was wise enough to know it. She liked his honest face and his open ways. Even his lack of tact was disarming in its naivety.

It was not wonderful that Elizabeth had lost her heart to such a personable young man. Could it be infatuation? She thought not. In some ways the child was older than her years.

She grimaced, imagining those frightful scenes among the wounded on the *Artemis*. Elizabeth had shown her mettle on that occasion. If it rested with her aunt, she should have her heart's desire.

Miss Grantham fell asleep with a smile of satisfaction on her lips.

It would have vanished if she had accompanied Elizabeth on the following day.

The outing began well enough. When the perch-phaeton drew up she had been ready for some time,

charmingly attired in her only redingote, and wearing the bonnet which Mrs Robsart had persuaded her
to buy in Portsmouth.

She found that a hot brick had been provided for
her comfort, and as Perry tucked a rug about her
knees she bestowed a smile upon him. She was
looking forward to the drive. Really, it was very
pleasant to be out of doors on this sunny winter's
day.

'You will not be too cold?' Perry looked down at
her as he took the reins and the carriage moved off.

'Thank you. I am perfectly comfortable. How
kind of the Earl of Brandon to let us use his phaeton!' Her dignified civility was intended to be quell-
ing, but Perry ignored her cool tone.

'Bang up to the minute, ain't it? I envy him his
team. They are real high-steppers... Old Frederick
is a notable whip, at least, he used to be. Now he
don't drive the phaeton much. His wife prefers a
barouche to a nasty, dangerous high-perch vehicle
which affords no privacy.'

Elizabeth chuckled. She guessed that he was quot-
ing his sister-in-law. 'It is dangerous?' she asked.

'Not unless I take a corner on one wheel, and I
don't plan to do that.'

She watched in silence as he guided the carriage
through the busy traffic. He was perfectly at ease
with the team of thoroughbreds, and they responded
to the skilled hands on their reins.

'Your mother is in good health, I trust?' she asked
at last.

'Certainly. She is looking forward to meeting you.
She remembers your father well.'

'When...when is she to call upon my aunt?'

'Tomorrow, I believe.'

Elizabeth felt a twinge of anxiety. How much had Perry told his family of her story? She hoped that he had been circumspect. The Dowager Countess of Brandon would be unlikely to look with favour upon a girl who had travelled from Genoa without a chaperon, and doubtless Sebastian's wife would feel the same.

Her chin went up. Why should she care for their opinion? It could not matter to her. If they wished to criticise, they might do so. She did not care a jot, except that her aunt would not be pleased with a slur upon her niece's reputation, or so she assured herself.

It was not strictly true. Elizabeth was beginning to realise that to stand well in the opinion of Society was important to her, and never more so than now, when she was about to meet Perry's mother.

He broke into her thoughts to point out that they were now driving along Piccadilly, and would soon be entering Hyde Park.

Elizabeth forgot her worries as she gazed at the crowds of folk who thronged the famous thoroughfare. Most of the pedestrians were men, and she could only marvel at their clothing.

'How do they turn their heads?' she murmured.

'What? Oh, you mean the shirt-points? With the utmost difficulty, I imagine. Look at that fellow over there! His collar is cutting into his cheekbones…'

Elizabeth giggled.

'I should not have worn my uniform,' Perry lamented. 'If I'd curled my hair and clad myself in yellow pantaloons and a rainbow-coloured waistcoat, I could have passed myself off as one of the dandy-set.'

'So you could,' she agreed wickedly. 'But it can't be helped.' Privately, she believed that none of the men about her could hold a candle to him. He looked like a gentleman, rather than a fribble.

'To make amends, I will take you into Bond Street. You have heard of it?'

'Aunt Mary says that I must do my shopping there.'

'You'll need a long purse, I fear.' He guided his team through the press of carriages, and was then hailed by a single horseman.

'Wentworth, by Gad! I thought I couldn't be mistaken. How do you go on? I thought you still on station in the Mediterranean.' The man's eyes fell upon Elizabeth and he checked his horse.

'Well, and who is this?' he asked softly. 'Wentworth, won't you present me to this lady?' He swept off his hat and bowed.

Perry's look was far from affable. 'Elizabeth, this is Lord Sholto Ashurst.'

'I am Elizabeth Grantham.' Her smile had an astonishing effect upon the gentleman. He turned his horse, and announced his intention to accompany them to the Park.

'Don't trouble yourself!' Perry gave him an ironic glance.

'No trouble at all, my dear chap! Mustn't neglect one of my oldest friends.' Lord Sholto gave Elizabeth a long look. 'At least I thought he was my friend. Now I'm not so sure. The sly dog has been keeping you to himself, I fear...'

Elizabeth warmed to his evident admiration. 'We are but just arrived in London, sir.'

'And you will take the town by storm. May I be the first to bid you welcome?'

'Not here, you won't. We're holding up the traffic.' Perry tried to wave his friend away, but his efforts were in vain. Matters did not improve when they entered the Park. They were soon surrounded by a crowd.

As compliments rained down upon her head, Elizabeth appealed to Perry.

'Must we stay?' she murmured in a low voice. 'Your friends are very kind, but I can't remember half the names. Besides, we are creating a disturbance. Some people over there are standing upon chairs.' Her face grew rosy with embarrassment.

Perry picked up the reins. 'I'll try to move on. Damme, if they ain't like flies round a honey-pot!'

As he urged his team away, they were hailed by a familiar voice. Elizabeth craned to see the speaker.

'It's Chris!' she cried. 'Oh, do stop, Perry!'

'Cut out by Rainham?' Ashurst asked. 'I won't have it, ma'am! You must beware of these sailors. They have a dreadful reputation...'

'No worse than yours, my Lord!' Chris shouldered his way through the crowd to reach Elizabeth's side. 'Go away, Ashurst! This lady is a friend of mine.'

'No, no! I won't be sunk by the navy. Ma'am, won't you send this encroaching creature to the rightabout?'

Elizabeth laughed heartily at this exchange. To be the centre of attraction had, at first, been overwhelming, but now she was beginning to enjoy it. It was most entertaining to listen to this delightful nonsense. She glanced at Perry, expecting him to share in her amusement, but he was strangely silent.

Then Chris took her hand. 'No need to ask how you go on, my dear. You are in famous looks. You are happy with your aunt?'

Elizabeth smiled at him. 'She isn't in the least what I expected.'

'Not a dragon?'

'She pretends to be, but she is very kind.'

'Then I may be allowed to call on you?'

'I'm sure she'd be delighted. No serving officer will be refused a welcome in her home.'

'Right then. Perhaps tomorrow?' He turned to Perry. 'Cat got your tongue, old lad? Or are you sickening for something?'

'I'm well enough to lay about me if this crowd don't move!' Perry snapped.

Chris pursed his lips in a silent whistle. 'Got out of bed on the wrong side today?' he asked. He turned away before Perry could reply to this outrageous suggestion, and dispersed the men about him by remarking that Miss Grantham was getting chilled.

As they melted away, Chris kissed her hand. Then he, too, was gone.

'Need you glare in quite that way?' Elizabeth demanded. 'I thought these people were your friends?'

'They are,' he growled. 'But they need not keep my horses waiting...'

'Oh! Is that the only reason why you are suddenly out of humour?'

'No, it isn't!' He jerked his head in the direction

of the groom. 'This is neither the time nor the place to discuss it.'

It wasn't until they reached the privacy of her aunt's home that he gave vent to his feelings.

'You had best take care,' he muttered darkly. 'It ain't at all the thing to flirt with all and sundry.'

'How dare you accuse me of flirting?' Elizabeth crimsoned to the ears with fury. 'I, at least, was civil to your friends, which you were not.'

'Too civil by half, madam! I promised your aunt that you would not be exposed to gossip.'

'It was you who took me to the Park,' she cried. 'Did you expect it to be empty?'

'No, I didn't, but there was no need…I mean…you might have hinted people away.'

Had she not known his opinion of her, she might have imagined that he was suffering from jealousy, but that, of course, was nonsensical.

'I am much obliged for your advice,' she told him in icy tones. 'I shall remember it. You need not fear a repetition of my poor behaviour. I shall not drive with you again.'

'Oh, come! I did not mean to criticise…just to warn you…' Perry realised that he had gone too far.

'I need no warnings from you, sir. What, I wonder, gives you the right to think that you may correct my conduct?'

'Why, nothing…nothing at all. I didn't mean to offend you. It was just that I thought…well… perhaps you understand—?'

'I understand that you are an arrogant, interfering busybody. You need not trouble to call again. I shall refuse to see you.' Elizabeth stalked away.

Perry's ordeal was not yet over. Miss Grantham met him in the hall. Her lifted eyebrows met with no response.

'At dagger-drawing again?' she enquired. 'Dear me! A four-year-old would go on better. Did your well-known tact desert you?'

'I haven't any,' Perry told her savagely.

'Well, my dear sir, you had best acquire some. What was it this time?'

Perry looked injured. 'I only ventured to give Elizabeth a hint. Everyone clustered about her in the Park, and, well…'

'Your own nose was out of joint? Wentworth, what did you expect? Elizabeth is a beauty. You can't be the only man to see it.'

'I might as well give up,' he said in gloomy tones. 'They all wish to call upon her. She may take her choice of offers, I expect.'

'That is more than likely,' Miss Grantham agreed. 'And you won't help your cause by quarrelling with her.'

'I won't get the chance! She won't speak to me again.'

The old lady chuckled. 'Why don't you accompany your mother when she calls tomorrow?' With that she dismissed him.

Later, she did not question Elizabeth about the outing, apart from a brief enquiry as to her first impressions of the London scene. Her main concern appeared to be the sad state of Elizabeth's wardrobe, in which the girl was obviously uninterested.

'But, my dear, you have barely a stitch to your back,' she protested. 'Lady Mountfield's daughter is

to come for you tomorrow, to take you shopping.
She leads a busy life, and it is good of her to spare
the time.'

Elizabeth was forced to agree, though she could
summon up no enthusiasm for the expedition.

She changed her mind when she met Mrs
Dalloway. The lady was so very elegant that her
own garments left much to be desired.

In spite of Bessie's efforts to wash and press her
gown, the fabric was looking sadly tired. Her redingote was not in the London style, and the bonnet
bought in Portsmouth lacked any claim to fashion.

Mrs Dalloway was too well-bred to betray surprise at Elizabeth's shabby clothing. The girl was
well-connected and, more importantly, she was an
heiress. A beauty, certainly, and lacking only a little
town-bronze. With her looks, any modiste in
London would be happy to dress her, and at a handsome discount, knowing that Miss Grantham would
show off her own creations to the best advantage.

She was a kindly soul, and Elizabeth took to her
at once. Between them, they spent a busy morning,
and by the time Elizabeth had ordered a number of
morning-gowns, an evening cloak, several dresses
suitable for balls, and a selection of devastating bonnets, Mrs Dalloway announced herself satisfied that
she would be able to go on quite well for the first
weeks of the Season.

'Aunt Mary, I have spent a fortune!' Elizabeth
sank into a chair and kicked off her demi-boots.
'Forgive me, please, but I think I have a blister on
this foot.'

'I know the feeling well,' Miss Grantham told her drily. 'Few things are more exhausting than a shopping expedition. I have avoided them for years.'

'Have...have there been any callers?'

'Dozens, my dear! You will find a number of cards and invitations...and flowers, too.'

'For me?' Elizabeth looked up in surprise.

'The bouquets are certainly not for me. Your appearance in the Park has brought half of London flocking to my door. Lord Christopher Rainham is a charming creature, is he not?'

'Chris? Oh, Lord, I had forgotten that he was to call. Aunt, I should have asked you first. I do beg your pardon, but I thought you would not mind. He, too, is an officer on the *Artemis*.'

'Quite right, my dear. He is an unexceptionable young man. What did you think of Lord Sholto Ashurst?'

Elizabeth twinkled at her. 'I thought he talked a lot of nonsense, ma'am, and so did his friends.'

Miss Grantham felt relieved. Her niece was no fool, and it seemed unlikely that her head would be turned by flattery. Elizabeth wasn't vain, but her beauty was outstanding, and in London gossip spread like wildfire.

By now, every mother of a hopeful son would have made enquiries about her niece. The fact that she was an heiress would bring the fortune-hunters too, but they would have her aunt to reckon with.

'Shall you drive out again tomorrow?' she enquired.

This apparently innocent question brought two pink spots of colour to Elizabeth's cheeks.

'I think not, Aunt,' she murmured.

Miss Grantham raised an eyebrow. 'You did not care for the Park?'

'Why, yes, of course, but it was crowded. Wentworth did not care to keep his horses standing...'

'I see! That would account for his odd manner yesterday.'

'Ma'am?'

'It was nothing,' her aunt replied in airy tones. 'Simply that when I spoke to him he seemed to be somewhat out of humour.'

'He is impossible!' Elizabeth cried in fury. 'He thinks himself a model of propriety, and he is not! He positively scowled at all his friends.'

'How strange! I find him well behaved...'

'You don't know him, ma'am. To be setting himself up as guardian, and to lecture me? I won't have it! He actually accused me of flirting!'

'Perhaps he is a little high in the instep because of his naval training...discipline, you know?'

'Well, I am not one of his crew, and he had best remember it. As for being high in the instep, Aunt, I wish you might have seen him in Genoa, climbing up a tree to busy himself in a matter which was none of his concern. He is much too fond of interfering.'

'A naval officer climbing trees? My dear, you astonish me! I must hope that he was not in uniform.' Miss Grantham kept her countenance only with the greatest difficulty.

'He was, and much he cared for that! I suppose he thought it a great lark.'

'Young men are not always wise, Elizabeth. They are strongly disposed towards adventure.'

'In future he may seek adventure where he will,'

her niece replied with dignity. 'He will not do so in my company. I shall not speak to him again.'

'That may be a little difficult, my love. Had you forgot? The Dowager Countess is to call on us today, and Wentworth will accompany her.'

# Chapter Eleven

Elizabeth was nonplussed. 'Must I meet her, Aunt?' she pleaded. 'I beg you to excuse me.'

'Certainly not. She is one of my oldest friends, and she will wish to make your acquaintance. To refuse would show a lack of breeding.'

'Yes, I suppose it would.' Elizabeth sighed. 'I'm sorry! I didn't mean to offend you.'

'You haven't done so, my love. Wentworth won't be a thorn in your flesh for long. When the refit of the *Artemis* is completed he will be off to sea again. Meantime, his mother will keep him fully occupied. She is anxious to see him wed.'

Elizabeth was startled. 'Why is that?' she demanded.

'Do you find it wonderful? Most parents wish to see their children happily settled, I believe.'

'I thought you disliked matchmaking mamas, Aunt Mary.'

'I don't class the Countess with them. She will look beyond money and a title. In fact, the girl she has in mind for Wentworth is as poor as a church-mouse, or so I am informed.'

'I wish her joy of him!' Elizabeth snapped. 'No, I don't mean that! Oh dear, I am becoming such a crosspatch...'

'You are tired, my dear. Rest now. Our guests will not arrive for several hours.'

This excellent advice went unheeded. Elizabeth found it impossible to rest.

To imagine Perry in the arms of another woman was more than she could bear. The idea had come as a shock to her. Yet the Dowager Countess of Brandon must have many friends, all of them with charming and biddable daughters. One or other of them must find favour in Perry's eyes. At his mother's urging, her youngest son would doubtless be persuaded to offer for the first delightful creature who took his fancy.

Behind the unwelcome thought lay another, deeper dread. The *Artemis* could not lie at Portsmouth docks for ever. Perry would receive orders to report back to his ship. Then he would be gone, to face all the dangers of battle.

She buried her face in her hands. He must not go away believing that she hated him. She must make amends. There was still time for that. Nothing...nothing he said in future would persuade her to fly out at him.

She lay back upon the day-bed, and closed her eyes. Luck had been against her from the start, she thought sadly. Since that fateful night in Genoa, everything had conspired to give Perry a dislike of her. Now it was unlikely that he would ever change his mind.

As her aunt had predicted, the rest restored her to

better spirits. They lifted even further with the arrival of a long-delayed letter from her father.

Mr Grantham sent fond love to both his sister and
Elizabeth. He also enclosed a letter of authorisation
to his London bankers, advising them that there
must be no limit upon Elizabeth's drawings for anything she might need.

He was happy to say that his wife was much improved in health, as he was himself. This he ascribed, in large part, to the knowledge that Elizabeth
must, by now, be safe in England.

Elizabeth was moved to protest. 'My father could
not be sure of that. There has been no time for my
letter to reach him.'

'He seems to have great faith in Wentworth's ca-
pabilities,' Miss Grantham murmured. 'Perhaps
some British ship has docked at Genoa, bringing the
news that the *Artemis* is safely come to Portsmouth.'

Elizabeth scanned the closely written sheets. 'Yes,
that is so!' Her lips curved in a smile of deep affection. 'Dear Papa! Here he begs my forgiveness for
his actions…as if I ever could think ill of him.' She
read on, then her colour deepened.

'Yes, my dear?' her aunt said encouragingly. 'Is
that all?'

'Not    quite!    He    mentioned    Perry…Mr
Wentworth… I am to thank him for his care of me,
and bid him remember my father's words. Oh, Aunt
Mary, I can't do that!'

'Why not, my love?' Miss Grantham composed
her features into an expression of surprise.

'Ma'am, I did explain. Papa tried to force Perry
into…into offering for me.' Elizabeth blushed
deeply.

'Force? I can't imagine it, my dear. That would be unlike your father. He may have suggested something of the kind, perhaps in desperation? It was a foolish idea. Young men prefer to choose their partners for themselves.'

Elizabeth was much struck by this remark. 'You think that is why he refused?'

'What else? You were strangers to each other, but you are no antidote, my dear. You won't believe that he refused because you have two heads, or a third eye in the middle of your forehead?'

Elizabeth smiled. 'No, I don't think that. It's just that he dislikes me, and has done so from the first.'

Miss Grantham forebore to marvel at the truth of the saying that love was blind.

'We must give him credit for one thing...'

'And what is that?'

'Clearly your fortune does not weigh with him. Many a younger son would have conquered his reluctance in the knowledge that you will be a wealthy woman.'

'I doubt if he knows of it,' Elizabeth told her stiffly.

'Possibly not. It cannot matter, as we are agreed, I think, that you and Wentworth would not suit.'

Elizabeth was silent.

'Now, my love, while you were resting, your purchases arrived from Bond Street. I have told Bessie that she may unpack them.'

'Shall you like to see them, Aunt?' Elizabeth was glad of the diversion.

The old lady nodded her approval as she slipped on a pelisse of French merino cloth, trimmed with braid. The matching bonnet was audaciously seductive, with its curtailed poke and curling feathers.

'Do you think it too outrageous?' Elizabeth asked anxiously.

'Not at all! It becomes you well.' Privately, Miss Grantham considered that this was an understatement. With her oval face framed by the dashing little bonnet, Elizabeth looked lovelier than ever.

'And these?' Her niece held up two filmy muslin gowns. 'Mrs Dalloway says that they are all the rage for evening wear. She reads *The Lady's Magazine or Entertaining Companion for the Fair Sex* to keep her up-to-date.'

Miss Grantham's lips twitched as she fingered the thin fabric. 'Dear me! Fully clad, your clothing is unlikely to weigh more than a couple of pounds.'

'She says that it is the classical influence... flowing draperies and such. You don't think them indecent?'

'Not if you wear an under-shift, my dear. I suppose we might lay in a supply of linctus against inflammation of the lungs.'

Elizabeth giggled. 'They *are* cut rather low in the bosom,' she admitted. 'But I bought a stole to wear about my shoulders.'

'And some walking dresses, I hope? The classical influence is well enough in its way, but the weather in Greece is somewhat warmer than it is in England.'

'I thought of that.' Elizabeth picked up a gown of heavy cambric, trimmed with frills of broad-lace. 'This has a matching spencer. That is a jacket, you know, which is worn for extra warmth.'

'Doubtless you will need it. I've known it to snow here as late as June.'

'Is that true? Perry said as much, but I didn't believe him. I've only seen snow in the distant mountains.'

'That is the best place for it. Here in town it is soon churned up by the carriages. Then it becomes a mass of grey slush, and galoshes must be worn.'

Dismayed, Elizabeth gazed at her satin demiboots with yellow gilt buttons, and another pair in rose-pink printed kid with loops and ties of silk ribbon.

'Will these be stout enough?' She pointed to a heavier pair in black morocco leather, with uppers of grey silk.

'They will serve if you wear protectors over them. Now, what will you wear today for Lady Brandon's visit?'

The decision was a difficult one. Must it be the charming sprigged muslin with tiny puff sleeves, or the high-necked gown of French worked cambric with the double flounce and rows of tucks? The pink silk was more suitable for evening wear, as were the half-dresses intended to be worn over slips of satin.

At length, after much deliberation, Elizabeth settled for a round robe in Pomona green. It was simple, but cut with such exquisite skill that it was clearly the work of the best modiste in London. Puffed at the shoulders, the long tight sleeves ended at the wrist with rows of tiny buttons.

The straight line of the drapery, falling from beneath the bosom, made her look taller, though she wished that the prevailing fashion for low edge heels or none at all had not robbed her of the opportunity to use her shoes to give her height.

It was mortifying to be so very small, but the gown was elegant, and no one would mistake her for a schoolroom miss, an impression which she wished most particularly to avoid.

And during these last few weeks her hair had grown, she thought with satisfaction. It still gave her the look of a Botticelli cherub, but in time she might wear it in a classical knot. It would give her the sophisticated appearance for which she longed. She'd often envied it in older women.

Yet sophistication was not the word which came to mind when she was introduced to Perry's mother.

The Dowager Countess of Brandon was dressed with such simplicity that Elizabeth was surprised. A second glance told her that the lady's garments were cut to perfection.

She smiled as she walked towards Elizabeth, holding out both her hands.

'At last, my dear!' she exclaimed in a low, musical voice. 'Perry has told me so much about you…'

Elizabeth avoided Perry's eyes.

'May I present you to my daughter-in-law, Lady Wentworth? Prudence, this is Elizabeth Grantham.'

The Dowager Countess was so tall that Elizabeth had not noticed the girl behind her, but now her ladyship came forward with an unaffected smile.

'I hope we shall be friends,' she said. 'I hear that you spent many weeks aboard the *Artemis*, with only Perry and Chris for company. Such a trial for you! Don't you agree, Mama?'

The Countess smiled. 'A dreadful ordeal!' she agreed. 'My dear, how did you cope with them?'

'Ma'am, they were very kind...' Elizabeth did not dare look at Perry.

'But the two of them together?' Prudence cried in mock amazement. 'Why, mischief is their middle name! Someday I will tell you of their goings-on. Perry was always ready for a lark. I doubt if he has changed.'

Perry was moved to speak at last. 'Pru, you might have mercy on me,' he protested. 'I've been trying to convince these ladies that I am a sober-sides.'

'You won't succeed. I imagine that they already have your measure.' She laughed aloud.

Elizabeth joined in the general amusement. She felt drawn at once to Lady Wentworth. This vivid, vital girl didn't look old enough to be the mother of two sons.

Prudence was no beauty, but there was a strangely arresting quality about her face, which was intriguing. It was hard to place, though it owed much to the light in the wonderful hazel eyes, her fine bone structure and the curving lines of that mobile, wilful mouth.

A lady of strong character, Elizabeth decided. Prudence would be a staunch friend, or an implacable enemy.

Now she was laughing up at Perry, pretending to beg his forgiveness for her forthright words. There seemed to be such easy camaraderie between them, and suddenly Elizabeth felt like an intruder.

Prudence sensed it at once, and drew Elizabeth into their conversation.

'Will you forgive us for our nonsense, Miss

Elizabeth? Perry has been my friend for some long time, though he does naught but tease me. Now I have paid him out by making him an uncle once again. I know it makes him feel like a greybeard.'

A general ripple of amusement followed this sally. Then Prudence made a suggestion, intended to give the two older ladies the opportunity for a private chat.

'Miss Grantham, will you think me forward if I ask to see your laboratory? If you allow it, we shall be very careful.'

'It is scarce a laboratory, my dear, though the shelves hold some specimens. Elizabeth will show you...' She bestowed a smile on Prudence, aware of the tact involved in the suggestion.

As the door closed behind the three young people, she looked at the Dowager Countess.

'Well, Jane, will they do?' she asked.

'I believe so. Elizabeth is delightful. You must have guessed that Perry is head over ears in love. As you can imagine, I couldn't wait to meet her. He speaks of nothing else, yet he says that she won't have him.'

'You know the circumstances?'

'Some of them, at least. I think he has not told me all.'

'We must give her time. She loves him, too. It is her pride which is keeping them apart.'

The Countess gave her a quizzical look. 'I can believe it. Perry isn't noted for his tact but he thinks the world of her. She is very lovely, though it is not that which has impressed him. He told me of their journey. Poor child! I thought she must have been afraid, but he says that she was not.'

A grim smile answered her. 'I doubt if she'd fear the devil himself. I could scarce believe that she had gone among the wounded as she did. My brother kept her sheltered.'

'As your father did with you?' The Dowager Countess chuckled. 'My dear Mary, blood will out! Even as a girl you surprised us all.'

'Stuff! I could not bear to be a milksop. And that awful Season! I did not take, you know.'

'I think you never wanted to, did you? When one's heart is given already...'

Mary Grantham looked at her friend, and when it came, her smile was painful. 'You knew? Strange, but it seems like yesterday, though it was fifty years ago. He was killed in the American colonies.'

'My dear, it has been hard for you. Have you found happiness at last?'

'I am content.' Miss Grantham shook her grizzled head as if to clear it of sad memories. 'Now, Jane, what are we to do?'

'You are sure of Elizabeth's feelings?'

'Certainly. Perry has no idea?'

'None! He thinks himself sunk beneath reproach in Elizabeth's eyes.'

The two ladies smiled at each other, in perfect agreement as to the folly of the young.

'It was unfortunate,' Miss Grantham admitted. 'The whole thing has been mishandled from the start. Perry was pressured into offering for her not once, but twice. I pointed out that it must go against the grain for any man of spirit, but she feels rejected.'

'But now, when it is his dearest wish to wed her?'

'She would not believe him, Jane. She is convinced that he dislikes her. They quarrel constantly…'

'I understand,' the Countess said drily. 'Perry was always a hothead where his emotions are concerned.' She rested her cheek upon one slender hand. 'I shall speak to Prudence. Perry has adored her since the day they met. She will think of something.'

'You think so highly of her?'

'I do, indeed, my dear. To see her now you would not think it, but her early life was passed in conditions that neither you nor I could well imagine. Orphaned at birth, she was thrown upon a parish in the north, and forced to work in a cotton mill.'

'Sebastian's wife? You cannot mean it!'

'Sadly, it is true. Until she was seventeen, she thought herself a bastard. She was running away when Sebastian found her, and brought her down to Kent. Then we discovered her true parentage…'

Miss Grantham looked a question.

'Yes, she is both well-born and legitimate. You will forgive me if I don't say more. I won't speak ill of the dead, and it is just history now.'

'Jane, you are to be congratulated. Both your sons are undeceived by outward appearance. They have chosen women of character.'

The Countess smiled faintly. 'I could wish that Frederick had done the same. You have not met Amelia?'

Miss Grantham shook her head. Then a glance of perfect understanding passed between them.

'Why not bring Elizabeth to the ball which Frederick is to give in Grosvenor Square next week?'

'Jane, you know how I feel about such gatherings. It's kind of you to suggest it, but I haven't attended one for years.'

'Then it's high time you did. Elizabeth must be considered, and I am asking for your support. Do say that you won't refuse...'

Miss Grantham wrinkled her nose and grimaced.

'My dear Jane, times have changed. You won't be exposed to the odour of unwashed humanity. Society actually bathes these days, since the advent of the Macaronis.'

'I'm glad to hear it,' her friend said with feeling. 'In my girlhood the stench was sometimes more than I could bear. Those exquisites were not just fashionable fribbles, then?'

'Their fashions were ridiculous, but they were clean.'

'Very well, you have convinced me. Brandon is a sensible man. I'd like to hear from his own lips if the Government is worried about revolution spreading to this country.'

'And Perry will have an opportunity to make his peace with Elizabeth,' the Countess observed slyly.

Unaware of the plans being made on their behalf, Perry and Elizabeth were standing either side of Prudence in Miss Grantham's study.

'Heavens, how grisly!' Prudence eyed the specimens with distaste. 'They would give me nightmares. I believe I'd rather see the garden. Let us leave Perry to improve his mind. I want to hear what you've been doing since you came to London.'

Elizabeth gave her a suspicious look. Was she to be quizzed about her time aboard the *Artemis*? The

Dowager Countess might have suggested questions which she did not care to ask herself.

At first, she answered only in monosyllables. Then Prudence turned to face her squarely.

'Don't you feel that you can trust me?' she asked in her forthright way. 'I'm not a spy for anyone, but you don't seem quite at ease.'

'I'm not!' Elizabeth was equally blunt. 'You may think me foolish, but you and the Countess can have no high opinion of me...'

'We think you very beautiful. As to the rest...we do not know you well, but that is easily remedied.'

Her friendly manner was encouraging, but Elizabeth turned away.

'I didn't mean that. My aunt informs me that in Society there are strict rules as to conduct... and...well...I travelled on the *Artemis* without a chaperon.'

This worthy attempt at honesty brought a peal of laughter from her companion.

'Great heavens, is that all? I almost went to sea myself, you know, but I was the victim of a press-gang.'

'Oh, no! I won't believe it! Women are not impressed—'

'I was dressed as a boy,' Prudence told her blithely.

'But why?' Elizabeth was round-eyed with astonishment.

'It's a long story. I'll tell you about it some time. I thought Sebastian loved someone else, so I decided to run away. I can't remember where now, but I think it was to Australia.'

'Alone?'

'I had a young friend with me. Dan was twelve or thirteen at the time.' Lost in thought, Prudence wound her finger about a curling feather in her bonnet. 'It all seems so long ago.'

Elizabeth looked at her with new respect. Prudence could be no more than five years older than herself. To all outward appearance she might be any young and fashionable young matron, yet there was a will of iron beneath the surface, and Elizabeth sensed it.

'I should not have doubted you,' she murmured. 'I won't make the same mistake again.'

'Plotting some mischief, are you?' Perry had wandered out to join them. 'One woman is bad enough, but when two get their heads together…?'

Elizabeth looked up, saw the twinkle in his eyes, and caught her breath. It wasn't fair. He had no right to be so handsome. When he looked as he did now, teasing, chaffing, and in the greatest good humour, it was impossible to resist his charm.

'We'll leave the mischief to you,' Prudence replied. 'You are something of a hand at it. We had best return indoors. Your mother will be wondering what has become of us.'

But Miss Grantham and the Dowager had not missed them. Their talk was all of the forthcoming ball.

Elizabeth gave her aunt a look of enquiry, but Miss Grantham was all smiles.

'Thanks to the Macaronis, and their notions, I am promised that I shall smell nothing more noxious than powders, perfumes and pomades. Such a relief, my dears, I have a nose for odours.'

Elizabeth was mystified. 'The Macaronis? What are they? In Italy, macaroni is a food...'

'And the Macaronis were the food of legend.' Perry grinned at her. 'Dandies to a man! Their wigs alone were the size of beehives, and they carried huge bouquets.'

'But they were obsessed by cleanliness,' his mother interjected, with a significant look at her hostess.

'Spotless!' Perry agreed. 'Where are they now, I wonder?'

'Transformed into worthy grandpapas, I should imagine.' The Countess rose to take her leave. 'Until next Thursday, then?' She bent to kiss her friend. 'Come, my dears, Frederick and Sebastian will be waiting!'

As the sound of their carriage faded into the distance, Elizabeth looked at her aunt.

'Shall you mind attending this ball, ma'am? If it is something you dislike...?'

'Not at all, my dear. I must not become a hermit. Besides, the Earl of Brandon is at the heart of Government. I shall be glad to speak to him.'

Elizabeth was doubtful. She suspected that Miss Grantham was considering her niece's pleasure.

'How good you are!' she said impulsively. 'I fear I don't deserve it.'

'Why not, my love?'

'Sometimes I am out of reason cross. Have I been a trial to you?'

'Not yet, Elizabeth. Tell me, how did you like our visitors?'

'Very much! The Countess is not at all what I expected. I feared she would be very grand.'

'Jane is a dear. When we were girls we were much in each other's company.' Her eyes lit up with a smile of reminiscence. 'And Prudence?'

'I thought her fascinating. She told me something of her early life. I could scarce believe it.'

'Yet Jane assures me that it's true. You are not the only girl to have adventures, you see.'

'Hers were truly dreadful…much, much worse than mine. She made me feel ashamed to be so missish.'

'Missish? I do not find you so. My dear, I'm happy that you have made a friend today.'

'Lady Wentworth said that I might call her Prudence, ma'am.' Elizabeth twinkled at her aunt. 'She thinks it a misnomer.'

'I don't doubt it. She is such a vital creature. I liked her open manner.'

She looked at Elizabeth's rosy face, still flushed with the pleasure of the visit. It was little short of a miracle that the child had turned out so well, reared, as she had been, without friends of her own age. Over-protected as she had been, and with only the company of her elderly father and his sick wife, she could have had little to amuse her.

Then she remembered certain of her ancestors and she began to chuckle.

'What is it, Aunt?'

'I was thinking of our own history. Someday, I will tell you the story of the distaff side. There is a certain curious streak of individuality which appears at intervals in the ladies of the Grantham family.'

Elizabeth could well believe it. She had not, in the past, met anyone remotely like her aunt.

'Now, my dear, will you forgive me if I leave

you? I have done no work today upon my treatise.'
With that Miss Grantham disappeared, and Elizabeth
was left to her own devices until the supper-hour.

She had much to occupy her mind. In the company of his family she'd seen Perry in a different
light. He'd seemed so easy, and so full of fun. But
behind the laughter there was something in his eyes.

She'd seen it when he joined them in the garden.
She'd turned and caught him unawares, to find that
there was a certain glow in his expression which she
found hard to understand. She might have thought
it tenderness had she not known better. She shook
her head. She must have imagined it. She was allowing her own longing to deceive her.

Yet when he spoke his voice had been almost a
caress. Could it be that he was changing his opinion
of her? A tiny flicker of hope stirred in her heart.

He had kissed her once, but that was long ago.
Perhaps he had forgotten it, but she had not. How
could she? The memory of his lips, warm and demanding, were imprinted on her heart for ever. Such
thoughts were deeply disturbing. She rang the bell
for Bessie.

'I haven't been paying much attention,' she announced. 'Did you unpack all my purchases?'

'Yes, miss. See, each drawer is labelled. Gloves
and stockings in here, scarves and shawls in the one
below, and your underthings in the top.' Bessie fingered the contents of that particular drawer with loving fingers. 'This gauze petticoat weighs no more
than a cobweb...'

Then she hesitated. 'Miss Elizabeth, shall you
wear these pantalettes? Some folk consider them im-
modest.'

'They are the latest fashion,' Elizabeth told her firmly. 'See, they are trimmed with lace, and very pretty.'

'But, miss, they are divided…like trousers.'

'I can't help that. I must wear something, after all, and next week, Bessie, I am to attend a ball.'

This exciting prospect banished all else from Bessie's mind. 'Have you decided what to wear?' she asked.

'Not yet. I had best look through my gowns again.'

This task kept Elizabeth occupied until she heard the dinner-gong. She was torn between an entrancing toilette consisting of an over-dress of spidergauze, to be worn over a slip of plain white satin, or a pink silk decorated with the serrated trimming known as '*Dents de loup*'. The teeth of a wolf seemed an odd description for the fine embroidery, but the cut of the garment was flawless, though the décolletage was very low.

'Is it too revealing?' Elizabeth studied her reflection in the mirror, concerned by the expanse of milky skin, and the way the bodice exposed the upper curve of her rounded breasts.

'No, miss! How lucky you are! You don't need false bosoms.'

Elizabeth was amused. She might appear half-naked, if she would forgo the immodesty of pantalettes. Still, she was undecided. Perhaps none of the gowns were suitable for the Earl of Brandon's ball.

A second shopping expedition seemed to be indicated, if she could persuade Mrs Dalloway to accompany her again. Then the humour of the situation struck her. For a girl who claimed to have no interest in the opinion of the *ton*, she was behaving like an idiot.

It was all self-delusion. She did not care about the *ton*. Perry's opinion was all that mattered. She wanted to look her best for him alone.

Suddenly, she felt bereft. It was only hours since she had seen him, but she missed him quite dreadfully.

Not for the first time she bewailed her hasty tongue and her quick temper. Why had she told him that she would not drive with him again? Now she must wait until the evening of the ball and on that occasion there would be no opportunity to speak to him alone.

Her hopes were raised next day. At the sound of carriage wheels she hurried to the window to find Chris at the reins of a smart racing curricle, with Perry up beside him.

She flew down the staircase on winged feet. Then she forced herself to a more decorous pace. It would not do to appear too eager.

'There you are, my love! Here is Wentworth come with an invitation for you.' Miss Grantham held out a note.

'My mother is getting up an expedition to Kew Gardens,' Perry explained. 'We are to take a pic-nic. Shall you care to join us?' His eyes were pleading.

'Tomorrow?' Her heart sank. She was promised to her aunt. Miss Grantham was most particularly anxious to attend a lecture upon anaesthesia.

'I'm sorry,' she said in a voice made cold by disappointment. 'We have another engagement.'

Perry's face fell. She had not forgiven him for his outburst. He felt wretched. All his efforts seemed to be in vain. He would never win her. Another engagement? He didn't doubt it. Doubtless, some suitor had persuaded her into looking upon him kindly.

It was Miss Grantham who took pity on him.

'You may make your choice, Elizabeth,' she said briskly. 'You must decide between the joys of a learned discourse upon the relief of pain, or a picnic by the river.' She managed to hide a smile.

'I will go with you, Aunt.'

'No, you won't, you foolish child! The fresh air will do you good.'

'Do you mean it, Aunt Mary? I did promise, but…well…I might not understand the finer points of the discussion.'

Miss Grantham looked grave. 'That is certainly a consideration. Let us agree that you will go to Kew.'

'Oh, thank you! I have always wanted to see the gardens.'

This information came as news to Miss Grantham, since Elizabeth had not mentioned it before, but she nodded and turned her attention to Lord Christopher.

That gentleman was not lacking in social graces.

'I hear that your group has been discussing the possibility of finding a safe method of anaesthesia, ma'am?'

'You are interested?' The old lady gave him a sharp look, wondering if he'd made the enquiry merely from politeness.

'Naturally! What a godsend it would be to all our wounded! At present we have only laudanum to ease their suffering. When that runs out, we resort to getting them drunk enough to bear the pain of amputations…'

Elizabeth shuddered, but his words were enough to launch Miss Grantham upon one of her favourite topics.

Under cover of the discussion, Perry turned to Elizabeth. 'You didn't mean it, did you? Forbidding me to call on you, I mean…?'

'I thought you had called upon my aunt,' she replied in a demure tone.

'Well, I did, of course, but the invitation to Kew was meant for you.'

'It was kind of Lady Brandon to wish to include me in her party. A pic-nic? What is that? It is unknown in Italy.'

'We eat out-of-doors, sitting on the grass. It isn't a formal occasion.'

'Is it not early in the year for that? Perhaps this is the custom here in England?'

Perry gave her his heart-stopping smile. 'It may be fine tomorrow, but I don't really care. Elizabeth, I wanted to apologise…to tell you that I had no right to speak out as I did. May we not be friends again?'

# *Chapter Twelve*

Elizabeth looked full into his eyes, and what she saw there set her pulses racing. She could not mistake the tenderness in his expression. Her colour rose, and she looked away, feeling strangely breathless.

'We cannot go to Kew as enemies,' she murmured. 'I spoke in haste...'

'So did I. I can't think what possessed me.' Perry devoured her with his eyes. 'It was unforgivable—'

'Yet you ask me to forgive you?' She had recovered some of her composure, and she was moved to tease him.

'Will you? I don't know why I lost my temper, but it won't happen again.'

'Will you swear to that?' She smiled.

'I mean it. Oh, Elizabeth...' Whatever he had been about to say was lost as Miss Grantham turned to him with an enquiry about the *Artemis*.

'We have heard nothing, ma'am. The refit must be taking longer than we had at first imagined.'

Miss Grantham nodded. Apparently absorbed in her discussion, she had been watching the two

young people. Now she considered that matters had
gone far enough. Perry's face wore a naked look of
love. He was in danger of saying too much, too
soon. She had warned him to go slowly.

Later there were other morning callers but, though
Elizabeth greeted them with her usual civility, she
could think of nothing except her love. Compared
with Perry, the beaux who showered her with invitations paled into insignificance. She could not even
recall their names when she and her aunt sat down
to a late nuncheon.

Miss Grantham returned to the subject of their
first discussion.

'I like Lord Christopher Rainham,' she announced. 'Such a sensible young man! In choosing
a husband you might do worse, my dear.'

Elizabeth blushed. 'I should have told you, Aunt
Mary. He offered for me when we were aboard the
*Artemis*.'

'Both he *and* Wentworth? The story of your voyage grows more interesting by the minute! Why did
you refuse him?'

'I don't love him, not in the way he wished. I'm
fond of him, of course. Chris is such a dear. He
helped to hide me, though both he and Perry might
have lost their preferment when I was discovered.'

'But that did not happen?'

'No, ma'am. When I explained to Captain
Robsart…'

'When you twisted him about your little finger,
you mean? What a puss you are, to be sure!'

Elizabeth's blush deepened. 'It wasn't anything

like that. I showed him Papa's letter. After that, he was very kind.'

'I see.'

'And then, you know, both Perry and Chris are fine officers,' Elizabeth continued in an earnest tone. 'Perry's seamanship is second to none, and Chris is the gunnery officer.'

'So he told me.' Privately, Miss Grantham considered it sad that any young man should devote his experience to weapons of destruction. Rainham should have been saving lives, instead of planning to end them. He was not insensitive. His interest in the relief of pain was genuine. A sigh escaped her lips.

'What is it, Aunt?'

'I was thinking only that in a perfect world there would be no need for gunnery officers.'

'But the world isn't perfect,' Elizabeth argued. 'Without her guns, the *Artemis* would have been blown out of the water.'

'I know it, but I cannot like the thought of war, and as I get older I like it even less.'

Impulsively, Elizabeth rose and kissed her. She was growing fond of her formidable aunt. 'You are sure you don't mind about the pic-nic? I can still cry off. I should be happy to go with you instead.'

'What a fib! I don't believe a word of it! Go back to your book, you minx! I shall take my work into the garden. You may join me, though you must not chatter.'

With this stern pronouncement, Miss Grantham departed to gather up her papers.

Elizabeth's unexpected gesture of affection had delighted her, though she did not show it.

For the rest of the afternoon they sat together in companionable silence, enjoying the unseasonal warmth of one of those fine spring days with which London was all too rarely blessed.

Elizabeth glanced at the cloudless sky. Would the weather hold? If it rained, the expedition to Kew would be called off, and the disappointment would be hard to bear.

She fell to dreaming, with her book lying unread in her lap. The flame of hope within her heart was growing stronger. Even now, she could not be quite sure, but this morning it had seemed that Perry was not indifferent to her.

She tried to crush the thought. Once before, aboard the *Artemis*, she had imagined something of the kind, only to find that she had been mistaken. It would be too cruel to suffer such a blow again.

'Are you enjoying your book?' her aunt enquired.

'Why, yes!' In her confusion Elizabeth dropped the volume to the ground. 'Have you read *Clarissa*, ma'am?'

'I have, but I think that you have not. In this last hour, you haven't turned a page.'

'I was wool-gathering,' Elizabeth admitted. 'Do you find that the breeze is growing chill? Perhaps we should go indoors...'

'You must not expect Italian weather here,' the old lady chided gently. It was clear that Elizabeth had no wish to be questioned as to the reason for her wandering thoughts. She could well guess at the subject which preoccupied the girl's mind, but she made no comment, other than to remark that it seemed likely that the fine weather would continue.

\* \* \*

In the event, this proved to be the case, and it was a merry party which set out on the road to Kew next day.

Perry led the way in the perch-phaeton, with Elizabeth beside him. Chris followed in a racing curricle, accompanied by a red-haired youth. A larger carriage, with the Brandon coat-of-arms emblazoned on the door panels, brought up the rear.

Elizabeth stared at the driver of this vehicle when she first saw him. This could only be Sebastian, Lord Wentworth. His resemblance to Perry was striking. That straight nose, the dark hair and eyes, the firm line of his jaw, and the full mouth, with its hint of sensuality, were unmistakable.

Perry noticed her surprise. 'That's m'brother. Ugly devil, ain't he? Wait till you see Frederick!' He lifted a hand in greeting to the occupants of the carriage.

Following his gesture, Elizabeth caught a glimpse of Prudence sitting opposite the Countess. The other passengers, both ladies, were unknown to her.

'I did not think we should be so large a party,' she murmured. 'Does the Countess enjoy a pic-nic?'

Perry smiled down at her. 'The pic-nic is not her main objective today. My mother is a dedicated gardener. In the usual way the only time she'll leave her home is in the dead of winter, when nothing will grow. The babes were a stronger draw this time, but I'll swear she sends instructions into Kent each day about her precious glasshouses.'

'They have such things at Kew?'

'The King's gardens are famous. He bought the house ten years ago, and the grounds are a delight.

Naturally, they are private, but Frederick obtained permission for my mother to see them.'

'I haven't met the ladies with her.'

Perry grimaced. 'The elder of the two is Mrs Aveton. Judith is her stepdaughter. My mother is fond of Judith.'

Elizabeth felt it best to make no further enquiries about the girl, though she was curious. Was the young Miss Aveton Perry's intended bride? It was a dispiriting thought. She couldn't resist one further question.

'Do you know Miss Aveton well?' she asked in a casual tone, hoping that he would regard this as no more than the polite interest of one guest in another.

'I've known her all my life,' Perry told her carelessly. 'She's quiet, you know. She don't get much of a look-in between her half-sisters and that dragon of a mother.'

Elizabeth glanced at him from the corner of her eye, and then she chuckled.

'You are hard on Mrs Aveton, sir.'

'I can't stand the woman,' he told her frankly. 'A harpy, if ever I saw one! What that poor girl goes through—' He stopped and gave Elizabeth a fleeting smile. 'I'm forgetting my promise to you...I was to moderate my tone today.'

Elizabeth changed the subject. 'Who is the young man with Chris?' she asked.

'Dan is Sebastian's adopted son. Didn't Prudence mention him?'

'She told me of a boy...a friend...who ran away with her.'

'That was Dan.'

'He looks very young. How long ago was that?'

'Let me see. It must be five years now. Dan would have been twelve years old, or possibly thirteen. They escaped from the mill together.'

'A mill?'

'A cotton mill in the north of England. They were little more than slaves. Dan oiled machinery, kept the looms in working order, and so on...'

'At twelve years old?'

'He'd been there since he was seven...sent by the parish, apparently.'

'That is barbaric!' Elizabeth's eyes flashed with indignation.

'It goes on still, and worse than ever. My brother has tried to put a stop to it in his part of the country.'

'And Prudence?'

'Prudence is a famous warrior for justice. She don't forget her early life. I shouldn't care to be the man she catches beating a child.'

'You think highly of her, don't you?'

'I do!' Perry's voice was warm with affection. 'Prudence has always stood my friend. We all love her. Straight as a die, old Prudence! With her it is pound-dealing, and she ain't afraid to speak her mind.'

'I can imagine!' Elizabeth looked at him with dancing eyes. So much for Perry's claim that women must not think. She knew his true opinion now. 'I like her very much,' she admitted.

'I'm glad to hear it... She's hoping to become a friend of yours, too.' The look he gave her made her heart turn over.

He looked as if he might have said more, but the

road had widened, and Chris whipped up his horses to draw alongside the phaeton.

'You'll be in trouble,' Perry called out cheerfully. 'Ain't you had your instructions? I was threatened if we took to racing.'

'Just overtaking you, old chap. If you drive much slower you'll come to a halt. It would have been quicker for you to walk.'

This insult could not be allowed to pass unchallenged, and Perry urged his horses to a faster pace.

'Do you mind?' he asked Elizabeth. 'If we let him overtake, we'll never hear the end of it.'

Laughing heartily, she shook her head. A slight breeze had brought the colour to her cheeks, and her eyes were sparkling with excitement. At that moment her pleasure was unalloyed. She wished that the drive might go on for ever.

All too soon they were within sight of Kew, and another few minutes brought them to a suitable pic-nic site beside the river.

Perry drew his team to a halt. As the grooms hurried to spread out rugs and assemble folding chairs for the ladies, he helped Elizabeth from the phaeton.

She stared at the number of baskets which were being laid upon the grass. There seemed to be food enough to feed an army. As bottles of wine were set to cool in a convenient pool, the party gathered in a flurry of introductions.

Prudence came to Elizabeth at once. 'I must hope that Perry didn't frighten you. When he whipped up, we were convinced that he would race in spite of all we'd said.'

'I wasn't afraid,' Elizabeth told her shyly.

'Then let me make you known to Mrs Aveton and her daughter, Judith.'

Elizabeth found herself under inspection from a pair of hard and button-like eyes. Mrs Aveton then became effusive in her compliments, but Elizabeth was not attending.

Her attention was fixed upon the tall and slender girl who stood a little to one side. Judith Aveton was no beauty, but there was character in that quiet face.

Her colouring was unremarkable. In fact, her smooth hair was of that indeterminate shade between blonde and brown, sometimes described as mousy. As she gave her hand to Elizabeth, her eyelids were lowered. Then she looked up and the effect was startling.

There was a luminous quality about those fine grey eyes, combined with a keen intelligence. The girl gave an odd impression of maturity, though Elizabeth guessed that she was little older than herself.

Then Mrs Aveton nudged her stepdaughter into making some conventional remark. Her words were brief, and to Elizabeth's mind she seemed to be preoccupied.

Was she cherishing a secret passion for Perry? There was no time to consider if it might be true, for at that moment Prudence beckoned to Sebastian.

'This is my husband,' she announced with pride. 'Sebastian, Miss Grantham deserves your sympathy. She was forced to suffer Perry's company for many a long week.'

'A trial, indeed, but you have borne it well, Miss Grantham. Your beauty has not suffered...' He smiled at her with all the family charm, drawing her into their circle, and making her feel less of a stranger. 'But what a fate for you! I hope you kept my brother in order?'

'If she did, it would be amazing!' Prudence asserted. 'We haven't managed it yet.'

'Pru, won't you give me credit?' Perry exclaimed in mock reproach. 'I am become a model of good behaviour. Dan, at least, will support me...'

The red-haired boy was bowing over her hand, and Elizabeth looked at him with interest. She had thought that he must be marked for life by his early trials, but the merry blue eyes gave no hint of it.

The entire party seemed determined to enjoy their expedition, and Elizabeth felt a growing pleasure in the company of this close-knit family. She joined in the merry chaffing, losing her initial shyness quickly.

As they settled down to eat, she marvelled again at the spread which lay before them. Pies and pastries flanked the platters of cold sliced beef and ham, and there was even a steaming casserole of mutton packed into a hay-box.

'That is for Dan,' Perry joked. 'He has a famous appetite.'

'I doubt if you'll refuse it, my dear,' his mother reproved. 'And nor will Lord Rainham or Sebastian. Miss Grantham, we don't stand on ceremony today. May I tempt you into trying a little of this dish?'

Elizabeth smiled her thanks, but she refused in favour of the pink and succulent ham, together with some salad. Then Perry approached her with a glass of wine.

'Champagne, Elizabeth? This is to celebrate your safe arrival in this country.'

As she took it from him, the others raised their glasses to her. She looked at their smiling faces, and felt a flow of warmth. At that moment, she longed for nothing more than to become a member of this happy family. If only she might be loved and cherished as Prudence was. Would such joy be always beyond her reach?

'The Gardens, Mama?' Prudence jumped to her feet when the meal was over.

'Presently, my love. I see you've been collecting bread. Don't you wish to feed the swans?' She and Mrs Aveton settled down to chat.

Prudence walked down to the river-bank and tossed scraps to the huge birds.

'We should have brought Thomas,' she murmured to Sebastian in a wistful tone. 'He would have enjoyed it so.'

'St James's Park is far enough for him,' Sebastian said comfortingly. 'Dearest, you know that he does not travel well...'

'I know. I'm being foolish, I expect.' Prudence looked up at her husband, and the loving glance which passed between them made Elizabeth look away. To speak to either at such a moment would have been an intrusion. She moved away.

Then Perry came to join her, bearing a napkin filled with broken rolls. 'Shall you care to feed these monsters?' he enquired.

Elizabeth backed away, but she was laughing. 'I don't think so. They are beautiful, or course, but those weaving heads remind me of serpents, and they are so close to us. Are they powerful?'

'The wings can break a man's arm. We'd best keep an eye on Dan. When something attracts his attention he is oblivious to danger.'

He glanced along the river-bank to where Chris and Judith Aveton were standing by a small craft. 'Where is the boy? I don't see him, do you?'

Sebastian hailed his brother. 'Does Miss Grantham wish to see the Gardens, Perry?'

'Go ahead! We'll follow you. I'll tell the others...'

He took Elizabeth's arm and began to hurry her away towards the river-craft. 'Drat the lad! I bet he's gone aboard that vessel.'

Elizabeth was the first to see Dan's flaming head, though it was at an odd angle.

'Blest if he ain't hanging out over the water.' Perry quickened his pace. His shout brought Dan back to dry land, but the lad was unabashed by Perry's warnings.

He sat down on the grass, took a notebook from his pocket, and began to draw.

'We've lost him now,' Perry announced. 'We shan't hear another word until he's worked it out.' He turned, took Elizabeth's arm, and began to retrace his steps.

'What is he doing?' she asked.

'Some detail of the boat's construction must have caught his fancy. He had always a passion for such things, even as a child.'

'I've left him to it.' Chris caught up with them. 'Miss Aveton says that she will bear him company.'

'Just as long as she ain't hoping for much conversation.' Perry glanced back at the couple. Judith was also seated on the grass, but she gazed ahead of her in silence.

She was an unusual person, Elizabeth decided. There was a contained quality in her manner... something which made her seem remote at times. Was she happy? Perhaps. Not everyone needed the stimulation of a crowd.

Perry led Elizabeth through the great iron gates and into the grounds of Kew. Ahead of her she could see the others in the distance, but he seemed to be in no hurry to catch up with them.

Chris looked at the faces of his two companions and left them to walk over to the lake, aware that tact was called for in this situation.

Elizabeth knew the reason for his sudden departure and it made her feel embarrassed. She quickened her pace.

'In a hurry?' Perry murmured. 'I thought you wished to see the plants...'

'I do, of course!' She coloured, only too conscious of the massive arm which held her to his side. 'What is this? Do you know the name?' She pointed to a clump of yellow flowers.

'Dandelions!' he said promptly.

'They are no such thing!' Elizabeth repressed a strong desire to giggle. 'The King would not cultivate weeds.'

'Daisies, then?' Perry's eyes were dancing.

'Daisies are white, as well you know. You must be serious, sir. It is an honour to be allowed to come here.'

'I am honoured enough to have you on my arm.'

'That is not the point,' she told him primly.

'Don't you wish to know the names of all these plants?'

'Not in the least! Other matters are closer to my heart. Tell me, have you enjoyed today?'

'Oh, very much!' she cried impulsively. 'This is all so new to me. How lucky you are to be a member of such a delightful family!'

He stopped then, turned to her and took her hands in his.

'I'm so glad you like them, Elizabeth. That is important to me.'

She did not dare to ask him why. Instead, she disengaged her hands, and attempted to move on.

'Don't go!' he whispered. 'Don't you wish to know the reason?'

'Perry, please! The others are coming back...'

He sighed. Then he looked up to find the rest of the party close at hand.

'My dears, I believe we should be starting back,' the Countess said reluctantly. 'As Mrs Aveton has pointed out, the air grows chill when the sun has gone.'

'No, no, my dear ma'am, I would not hurry you away for worlds. This has been so instructive...' The hard eyes roved over the little group. 'Where is Judith?' she demanded.

'We left her sitting by the river, Mrs Aveton.' Elizabeth was aware of the sharp look on the older woman's face.

'Alone?'

'Of course not,' Perry replied. 'Dan is with her.'

'Indeed!' Her tone caused Prudence to swing round.

'You have some objection, Mrs Aveton?'

'My dear Lady Wentworth, pray don't take me up so for my concern about my darling girl. Dearest Judith! A joy to us, of course, but sadly given to wool-gathering, I fear. I had made sure that she would like to see the plants...and now, you see, she has missed her chance.'

'And enjoyed a little welcome peace, I fancy,' Perry murmured to Elizabeth.

She did not reply, sensing at once that Mrs Aveton saw her as a serious rival to her quiet step-daughter. That lady was quick to turn the situation to her own advantage.

'Ah, well, it can't be helped,' she sighed. 'We cannot wait for her in this chill wind, and with Miss Grantham lately come from the warmth of Italy, she must ride back with us. Mr Wentworth, shall you object to fetching Judith back to London in your carriage? The naughty child has no idea of the trouble she has caused.'

'No trouble at all, ma'am!' Perry's tone was distant. 'It will be a pleasure.' He hid his disappointment with good grace.

Under cover of their departure, he drew Elizabeth aside. 'This wasn't what I intended,' he murmured. 'Will you drive with me tomorrow?'

'Not tomorrow,' she said quietly.

'You have a previous engagement?'

'I have a duty to my aunt. I must bear her company.'

'Another meeting?'

Elizabeth laughed. 'I don't know yet, but I don't...don't wish to make use of her. Do you understand? It would be wrong to use her home as a hotel.'

He nodded. He was disappointed, but he could understand her scruples.

The Countess was pleased. She had overheard the exchange and it confirmed her good opinion of Elizabeth, who at no time during the day had betrayed the fact that she thought of Perry as more than a friend. Her attention had been given equally to the other members of the party, even in the face of Mrs Aveton's obvious hostility.

That lady's suggestion that she should ride back in the carriage with the other ladies had confirmed it. Now Mrs Aveton bustled about, urging Elizabeth to take the corner seat.

Elizabeth was amused by, in spite, or possibly because of, the older woman's tactics. She was anxious to leave before Judith reappeared, but she was too late.

As Dan and Judith walked towards them, Elizabeth surprised a look of hatred on Mrs Aveton's face. Aware that she was under scrutiny, the look was banished at once.

'Too late, my dearest love!' she cried. 'You are to brave the cold with Mr Wentworth, you naughty puss!'

Judith seemed about to speak, then her eyes rested briefly on Elizabeth's face. The smile she saw there eased her mind, and she turned back to Perry.

'Now we shall be comfortable,' Mrs Aveton cried. Again she looked at Dan with an expression of distaste. He bowed as the carriage rolled away, but she ignored him.

Elizabeth felt indignant. It was clear that Mrs Aveton disliked Dan, though why she couldn't imagine. After all, he was just a boy. There could be no harm in his speaking to her stepdaughter. She guessed that Judith was in for a severe scolding later in the day.

Beside her, Prudence had stiffened. It was clear that she was controlling her temper only with the greatest effort. Her replies to Mrs Aveton verged on the abrupt, and Elizabeth thought it prudent to question her about her children.

This served to lighten the tense atmosphere inside the coach, though the Countess eyed her daughter-in-law in some concern. Thankfully, the rest of the journey was accomplished without the explosion which she feared.

It was not until Mrs Aveton had been set down that Prudence gave full vent to her feelings.

'Mama, you must forgive me! I know that creature is a friend of yours, but did you see the way she looked at Dan? He might have crawled from beneath some stone.'

'She is a stupid woman, Prudence. I don't regard her as a friend, more as an acquaintance. I invited her today because of Judith. The girl is so badly treated...'

'That doesn't surprise me! What a harridan! She must be a fiend to live with!' She stopped and looked at Elizabeth. Then she began to smile. 'Now you see me in my true colours. My hasty temper is a heavy cross for my family to bear.'

Elizabeth returned her smile. 'Mine is dreadful,' she admitted. 'I try to control it, but sometimes I fly into the boughs.'

Having confessed their faults, the two girls looked at the Countess to find that her eyes were twinkling.

'Such a pair!' she teased. 'What am I to do with you? Shall you bring pistols to the ball, instead of reticules?'

'No, no, we shall be very good! I shall practice my downing stare. That should be enough to strike terror into the hearts of my enemies.'

'You have none, my love. Take care, or you will give Elizabeth the wrong impression of our acquaintance. They are not all Gorgons!'

Upon this cheerful note they left Elizabeth at Miss Grantham's door.

'Thank you!' the Countess murmured. She was sensible of the fact that it was Elizabeth who had averted an ugly scene with Mrs Aveton. On an impulse, she bent and kissed the girl. Perry had chosen well. If only he might be successful in his wooing.

Elizabeth hurried to her room. Miss Grantham had not yet returned, and she was glad to be alone. She needed time to think...to dwell upon the events of the past few hours. This was a day she would remember all her life.

Curled up in the windowseat, she called to memory Perry's every word and look. There had been a sense of urgency in his manner, combined with gentle tenderness which made her pulses race.

When they'd walked together she had been so aware of his closeness...of the pressure of his arm in hers. Those moments had a dreamlike quality. Had it really happened, or had she imagined it? Suddenly, she was floating, seeming to see the world about her for the first time.

Now she could not wait for their next meeting. It had taken all her strength of will to refuse his invitation for the following day. She would not see him again until the night of the Earl of Brandon's ball, and how the days would drag without him! Meantime, she must not upset her aunt by mooning about the house.

That evening Miss Grantham announced her intention to break the habit of a lifetime. For the Earl of Brandon's ball she would appear in a fashionable toilette.

'There's no fool like an old fool!' she announced with a wry smile. 'But I owe it to you, my love. Your aunt must not be seen as a figure of fun.'

Elizabeth protested warmly. 'You would never be that, Aunt Mary. Am I to go shopping with you?'

'If you please, Elizabeth. I am quite out of touch with the present style. In my day we wore hoops, and stays which pinched us cruelly. Thank heavens the fashion for powdering is gone. I well recall some of the more outrageous creations, with hair built up to two feet or more in height.'

Elizabeth refused to believe it.

'But it is true, my dear. Ladies were forced to sleep in a sitting position. One heard some alarming stories. A pomaded head lay often undisturbed for several months. When it was taken down it was sometimes full of vermin, including, in one case that I heard of, a mouse.'

Elizabeth squealed in horror. 'I should have hated it!'

'As I did myself. It was a filthy habit. You see, now, why I believe that cleanliness is all?'

Elizabeth was intrigued, wondering what her aunt would make of the light poplins, muslins, tulles and filmy gauzes so fashionable with the *ton*.

* * *

On the following day, Miss Grantham dismissed them from her consideration with a peremptory wave of her hand. She was then informed by the modiste that the hoop and wide skirt still survived, but only in Court circles. For the Earl of Brandon's ball they must be considered suitable. She had heard a rumour that the Prince of Wales intended to be present.

Miss Grantham was unimpressed. 'I have done with hoops,' she said briskly. 'Ridiculous! One might as well carry a house upon one's person...'

For a few anxious moments it seemed that the shopping expedition would be a failure. Then Madame Céline was inspired to suggest a half-dress of the finest parchment-coloured Brussels lace, to be worn over a gown of heavy silk brocade in the same shade.

'Well, Elizabeth?' Miss Grantham cocked an eyebrow at her niece.

'Aunt, it is so beautiful!' Elizabeth stroked the fabric with loving fingers. 'And this shawl! It is a perfect match. See how well it looks!'

'So it should!' Miss Grantham threw her eyes to heaven. 'Fifty guineas for a shawl! Why, my dear, it would buy a microscope!'

Elizabeth laughed. 'You cannot wear a microscope about your shoulders, ma'am.'

'I'll take them!' Miss Grantham turned to Madame Céline. 'You have a turban or some such thing to wear upon my head?'

Happy in the knowledge that she had just sold the most expensive toilette in her entire establishment, Madame Céline hurried to produce a range of caps adorned with jewelled aigrettes, gilded circlets designed to nestle within a crop of curls, and various turbans of terrifying size and splendor.

'This will do!' Miss Grantham seized a turban and crammed it on her head, much to the modiste's satisfaction. This final purchase was also hideously expensive, but her unusual customer seemed untroubled by the cost.

With many expressions of gratitude for their custom, and in hopes of a return visit, Madame Céline bowed them to their carriage.

'A return visit? Ha! She will wait long enough for that,' Miss Grantham announced.

'Everything *was* expensive,' Elizabeth admitted. 'I feel so guilty, Aunt. Had it not been for me, you would not have felt obliged to spend the money.'

'Stuff!' Surprisingly, Miss Grantham seemed pleased with all her purchases. 'I have a fancy to appear in all my finery, especially since the present fashions are so comfortable. Now, what do you say to a drive this afternoon?'

Elizabeth was quick to agree. She might catch a glimpse of Perry in the Park, though it seemed unlikely. More probably he would be at Tattersalls, at Gentleman Jackson's saloon, or at one of the clubs in St James's Street.

If only he had not been recalled to Portsmouth. She was on tenterhooks as they returned to Mount Street.

## Chapter Thirteen

It eased her mind to find that there was no message from him. He would not leave without bidding them farewell.

If only he might remain in London for the ball. It was her dearest wish. In these last few days she'd sensed a difference in his manner towards her. Twice, he had been on the verge of saying...what? She did not know, and could not guess.

It could have been another apology, or had he been about to tell her that he was to marry Judith Aveton? She crushed the unwelcome thought. Perry had betrayed no particular interest in the girl, and had driven her back to London with him only at Mrs Aveton's insistence.

It wasn't what he'd intended. He'd told her so himself, but what did he intend? Hope blossomed in her heart. Suppose he should propose to her again? He was under no coercion. This time it would be of his own free will, and she would not throw the chance of happiness away.

On the day of the ball she felt a nervous fluttering in the pit of her stomach. Would this evening seal her fate? How missish to be trembling like some foolish schoolgirl, when she wished to present an appearance of dignity to the world.

She summoned all her resolution as she and Miss Grantham climbed the staircase of the house in Grosvenor Square.

The Earl of Brandon, flanked by his family, headed the reception line, and he greeted her aunt with extreme courtesy, holding her in conversation, and promising himself the pleasure of a long talk with her later in the evening.

Miss Grantham introduced Elizabeth, who looked at him with interest, thinking, as she did so, that this family was a race of giants. Tall though their mother was, the Earl of Brandon and Sebastian topped her by several inches, and Perry towered above them all.

As Elizabeth made her curtsy, she found herself under scrutiny by a sharp-featured woman standing beside the Earl. This must be his wife, Amelia.

She remembered Perry's acid comments on the lady's nature, but Amelia offered a gracious welcome. Elizabeth was surprised, and stole a glance at Perry, to find much amusement in his look. Then she understood. Not only was she the niece of the formidable Miss Grantham, but she was also an heiress, a sure passport to favour in these exalted circles.

'You are honoured,' Prudence whispered further along the line. There was no need to say more. With her quick intelligence Prudence was in no doubt as to the reasons for Amelia's singular cordiality.

'I know it.' Prudence returned Elizabeth's smile as she moved to join the other guests.

She gazed at the milling throng in wonder. The

ladies were all *en grande toilette*. In the centre of
one group of gentlemen she saw a girl whose limbs
were clearly visible beneath a gown of shimmering
gauze.

Another daring creature sat with her legs spread
apart, and her drawers on display. Beside her stood
a woman of voluptuous appearance, clad in flesh-
coloured pantaloons. Her over-dress was drawn up
at each side, exposing her legs as far as the thigh.

'What on earth are we coming to?' Miss
Grantham snorted her disgust at such wanton behaviour. 'Those hussies might as well be naked!'

Elizabeth made no comment. Her own gown had
met with her aunt's approval. Now she was glad that
she had chosen to wear the plain white satin, with
its over-dress of spider gauze. Simple in cut, it was
the perfect foil for her startling beauty, though she
was not aware of it until Perry came to claim her
for a dance. The look in his eyes was tribute enough.

Wisely, he did not disconcert her with fulsome
compliments. He led her out with only the briefest
pressure of his hand.

Like many large men, he was light on his feet and
danced extremely well. When he spoke at last, it was
to tease her gently.

'It is usual to converse politely with your partner,
ma'am.'

Elizabeth blushed. 'This is my first ball,' she explained. 'I must mind my steps.'

'You are a natural. Why not relax and let me lead
you?'

'Oh, yes! I love to dance.'

Looking at her, he could well believe it. Her little
oval face was alight with pleasure and, as she looked

up at him, her expression caused his heart to miss a beat.

'Elizabeth, if you smile at me like that, you will distract me…'

'Oh!' It was an inadequate reply, and Elizabeth knew it. She looked away.

'Too many people here!' Perry looked about him. 'I shall lose you in this crush. Don't you find it over-warm?'

Elizabeth nodded. The Earl of Brandon's mansion seemed to her to be at hothouse temperature.

'It's for the Prince's benefit,' Perry explained. 'He dislikes cool rooms.'

'He is expected here tonight?'

'He may look in. If so, Frederick will present you.' He sensed her shyness at this awesome prospect, and when the dance ended he led her to a seat behind a pillar.

'Would you like some lemonade?' he asked.

Elizabeth nodded. Her throat was dry and she found it difficult to swallow. The thought of meeting the heir to the throne had overset her composure. She had heard so much about his early promise, his youthful passion for the actress Mrs Robinson, those fatal letters to his 'Perdita' from her 'Florizel', and the huge sum it had cost his father to rescue Prince George from his promises.

Known as 'The First Gentleman of Europe', would he prove to be as handsome and as charming as his reputation suggested?

Then her chin went up. The Prince was a man like any other, and neither in speech nor manner would she betray her nervousness. She must not disgrace her aunt.

Besides, she would have Perry with her. The Prince, she was convinced, would never outshine him.

Her lips curled. The Prince might be a social lion, but she need not fear his claws.

Then she jumped as a hand touched the bare flesh of her shoulder.

'Elizabeth, my only love! Tonight, you are more beautiful than ever!' The man who spoke had been standing behind her. Now he came to join her on the sofa.

'*Cesare!*' Elizabeth could not believe her eyes. 'What are you doing here?' At first she thought she must be dreaming, but the man beside her was no figment of her imagination.

'I'm with the suite of the Italian Ambassador. Oh, my darling, it has been so long.' The Count seized her hand and raised it to his lips.

She snatched it away as if she had been stung. 'Stop! You mustn't! And pray don't call me your darling!'

'So cold, my dearest? Did you think that I would never reach you? Believe me, I came as quickly as I could.'

'You shouldn't have done so,' Elizabeth said sharply. 'There was not the least need...' She was irritated by his sentimental tone. To her ears it sounded false.

'You have not forgiven me for deserting you?' The liquid eyes swept her from head to toe, and she had the uncomfortable sensation of being stripped of all her clothing.

'Don't be so foolish!' she snapped. 'You must not

say such things to me. If my partner should return—'

'The Englishman? His mission will keep him occupied for some time. There is a sad crush in the dining-room.'

'My aunt is here. She will think it odd to find me speaking to a stranger.'

'How you have changed, my dear! You did not used to be so careful of the proprieties.' It was a clear reference to that night in Genoa when he had climbed up to her balcony.

Hot colour flooded Elizabeth's face, but she made a quick recovery.

'We are in London now. Cesare, please go!'

'But I have so much to say to you! Come, let us dance! That, surely, is acceptable?'

Elizabeth shook her head in violent disagreement, but she could not escape him. The strength of his grip upon her wrist made her wince with pain. It was impossible to release herself without a struggle, and that would attract attention.

With a stony expression she allowed him to lead her out.

'That's better! Tell me, dearest, how do you go on? Your father must have lost his reason to send you away like that.'

'You will please not to criticise my father, and I am not your dearest,' Elizabeth hissed. Trembling with anger, she eyed him with dislike.

The Count was dressed in the height of fashion. He was hung about with fobs and gold chains. A ruby the size of a pigeon's egg adorned his cravat, and his waistcoat was of a dazzling hue.

Now he was smiling down at her in a way which

made her fume. His look was both patronising and proprietorial. How could she ever have believed herself to be in love with him?

He ignored her angry tone. 'The English climate agrees with you. You are in famous looks tonight. Or is there another reason? You will not tell me that you cherish a *tendre* for that great blockhead who has been squiring you about? I saw you in Hyde Park, and again at Kew.'

Elizabeth was startled. 'Have you been spying on me?'

'Merely taking an interest in your friends, my dear. My wife's good name must be my first concern.'

Her blood ran cold. 'Your wife? Are you mad? You know my father's feelings. He has forbidden you to speak to me.'

The Count's expression was sentimental. 'Did we not agree that we should not let that weigh with us? You cannot have forgotten.'

'Let me go!' She tried to pull away, but he would not release her.

'Take care!' His face grew stern. 'You are attracting curious looks. As my betrothed, you must learn to behave with more decorum.'

'I am not your betrothed,' she cried in panic.

'Odd! I was under the impression that you were, or has the gallant officer supplanted me? He left us early on that night, you will recall. What would he say, I wonder, if he learned that you had admitted me to your bedchamber?'

Elizabeth felt sick with dread. 'It isn't true!' she whispered. 'I sent you away.'

'Will he believe you? You told him in my hearing

that I was a friend of yours. The Lieutenant does not strike me as a moderate man.'

'He isn't!' she cried. 'More than likely he will beat you to a pulp.'

'I doubt it! Will he wish to cause you pain with an attack upon your loved one?'

'You are not my loved one. How often must I tell you? Cesare, I was just a foolish child. Surely you will not hold me to my promise...'

'There you are mistaken, dearest.' The superior smile appeared once more. 'You will wed me, Elizabeth. I have not come so far to find myself rejected.'

'I won't! I won't!' Her voice was rising in hysteria.

'Then you must be prepared to take the consequences. When I tell my story in certain quarters, you will no longer be received in London, and nor will your aunt. Such a sad blow for your paramour!'

'You would not dare!' She stared at him in horror.

'Indeed, I would! Think about it!' The Count looked about him. 'The music has stopped. You may go now.'

Elizabeth stumbled away from him. Frantic to escape, she concealed herself behind a pillar and sank on to a nearby sofa. She could see no sign of Perry or her aunt.

There, she pressed a hand to her aching brow, knowing that her world was in ruins.

'Are you quite well, Miss Grantham?' Judith Aveton came to sit beside her. 'You look a little pale.'

'It...it is the heat, I expect. Perry went to fetch

me some lemonade, but I don't see him anywhere.'
Elizabeth felt that she was babbling.

'It *is* very warm. Many people have gone on the
same errand, which must cause a delay. You do not
mind the crowds?'

It was difficult to pay attention when her mind
was racing, but Elizabeth forced herself to reply.

'Not in the least. Do you?'

'I am an oddity, Miss Grantham. I never feel so
lonely as when I am in a crowd. You will think me
strange.'

'Please call me Elizabeth. I don't find you strange
at all. You seem to me to have an inner strength.'

'It is often sorely tried.' The grey eyes twinkled
at her companion. 'And I am given to daydreaming,
even at a ball. It is a sad weakness, and has caused
me to lose my sisters in this crush.'

Elizabeth was grateful to this quiet girl, who had
come to her simply out of kindness and concern.
The conversation, trivial though it was, had given
her time to recover her composure to some small
extent. Then she looked up at the mention of her
own name. It came from behind the pillar.

'Does Miss Elizabeth Grantham know her recent
partner well?' a deep voice enquired.

'Elizabeth? I don't know. Was she dancing? I left
her here to wait for me.' It was Perry who replied.
'Why do you ask? Is something wrong?'

'You must just drop a word of warning in her ear.
The Count is well-known to our agents in Italy.'

'The Count. Which Count?' Perry sounded mystified.

'Count Cesare di Tavola. He claims to be attached

to his Ambassador's suite. We know, however, that he is but lately come from France.'

'What do you know of him?' Perry's voice was icy, and Elizabeth's heart sank.

'Just that he will bear watching. He sells information to the highest bidder. We suspect that many of the sinkings in the Mediterranean must be laid at his door.'

'But he is Italian, not French, and we are not at war with Italy.'

'He is no patriot, Perry.' The Earl of Brandon's voice was grave. 'The French are his masters now, and they pay him well.'

Elizabeth huddled further into the corner of the sofa, trying to make herself as inconspicuous as possible.

'They can't see you,' Judith observed quietly. 'This pillar is in the way.'

'Excuse me, please!' Overcome with nausea, Elizabeth fled with a handkerchief to her lips.

Cesare was a spy. Now she understood why he could afford to dress so well, and to adorn himself with such expensive gew-gaws.

All bought with blood money, she thought wildly. How could he send men to their deaths for the sake of a few bags of gold?

There was no hope for her. She knew that now. If money was his god, she would never be allowed to escape him.

Was this to be her punishment for a brief infatuation? Was she to be made to pay for her folly for the rest of her life?

Cesare had made no idle threats. Such a ruthless

opportunist would let nothing stand in his way. And she had imagined that he loved her.

Now she knew the truth, and it was bitter to realise that he wanted her only for her father's wealth. What a fool she'd been. If he'd cared for her at all, he would have accepted her refusal, and wished only for her happiness.

She must find her aunt, and ask to be taken back to Mount Street. Aunt Mary would hide her. Then she remembered Cesare's threats. She had no doubt that he would carry them out. Miss Grantham would be shunned as the relative of a wanton who gave her favours freely.

Her own grief was too deep for tears. She loved her aunt. How could she destroy that lady's good name? It was poor recompense for kindness.

Blindly, she pushed open the nearest door, and found herself in a book-lined study. Now she needed all her courage if she were to face Perry again.

She writhed in anguish as she recalled the anger in his voice. It was true. She had told him herself that she was betrothed to Cesare. Could she deny it? And would he believe her if she did so? It was too much to hope.

She found that she was shaking uncontrollably. The shock of seeing Cesare again had been severe. Worse was the knowledge that he intended to destroy her. Her fate would be equally vile, whether she married him or not.

She pressed her hands to her burning temples, remembering his threats. She didn't lack courage, but how was she to deal with blackmail?

Thankful for the fact that only a single lamp was burning in the study, she crept to the far corner of

the room. If the door opened, no one would see her
in the wing-backed chair. She felt like some terrified
animal, pursued by a deadly predator.

She fought a rising sense of panic. She would *not*
wed Cesare. She could not. If only she'd been a
man. Then she could have run a sword through his
black heart. But no one could help her now.

She froze as the door swung open. Was it Cesare?
Had he come to find her, demanding her acceptance
of his proposal? She would need all her courage
now. She must think of some way to play for time,
to put him off until she had considered what to do.

'Elizabeth?' Perry's deep voice startled her. She
jumped, causing the chair to creak.

He reached her in a few long strides, and swung
her round to face him.

'Your aunt has been searching for you. May I take
you to her?' His face might have been carved in
stone.

Elizabeth tried to rise, but her legs would not support her.

'Oh, come! You must not allow the sight of your
lover to cause you to faint.' Perry addressed her as
if she were a stranger. 'Where is the gentleman, by
the way?'

'I don't know,' Elizabeth whispered. 'I came in
here to hide from him.'

'A likely story! You danced with him, I believe?'

'I had no choice.' She thrust her wrist towards the
light. The marks of Cesare's fingers were still visible
on the milky skin.

'He did that? What an affair you must have had,
if rough handling takes your fancy.'

'You don't understand.' The tears were rolling

unchecked down her cheeks. 'He hurt me when I tried to get away.'

Then Perry was on his knees beside her.

'Ah, don't, my darling! I can't bear it! Why didn't you call to me?'

'I couldn't see you...' she choked out. 'Oh, Perry, you must believe me!'

'Come here!' Perry took her hands and raised her to her feet. Then he slipped a hand beneath her chin and turned up the little tear-stained face to his. When his mouth came down on hers the world was lost to both of them.

It was long before he released her, and in those moments their past disagreements were forgotten in an overwhelming tide of passion which swept away everything but their love.

Elizabeth could only cling to him. She didn't trust herself to speak.

Then Perry sat down and took her on his knee, raining butterfly kisses upon her brow, her eyelids and her cheeks.

'I have disobeyed your aunt, my love. I promised to wait...to give you time to know your heart. It was impossible. Oh, Elizabeth, I've loved you for so long. Tell me I'm not mistaken, and that you feel the same?'

'You know it.' With the simplicity of a child she lifted up her face for his kiss. His lips were warm and tender, and she abandoned herself to that caress in unrestrained delight.

She thought he would never let her go, but he held her away from him at last, and looked deep into her eyes.

'We have wasted too much time,' he murmured. 'When shall we be wed?'

Marriage? Elizabeth stiffened as memory returned.

That very evening another man had insisted on it, and she had no doubt that the Count would carry out his threats if he risked losing his wealthy prize.

If she accepted Perry he would protect her, but at what cost? When gossip about her reached his ears there would always be that little worm of doubt, eating away at his heart, no matter how he attempted to refute the rumours. He deserved better than that.

She looked down at the beloved head. Now his lips were pressed against the palm of her hand. Very gently she withdrew it from his grasp.

'My love?' Perry looked up in surprise. 'You have not answered me.'

'We must not be too hasty.' She found it difficult to control her voice. 'I must have my father's permission—'

'Goose! He has given it already. Nothing would please him more.' Perry smiled down at her.

Elizabeth shook her head. 'When he approached you, it was out of desperation. He may have changed his mind now that I am safe in England.'

She hated herself for the prevarication. She should have had the courage to tell Perry that she could never become his wife, but she could not do it. Even now, at the last, she was hoping for some miracle which would remove Cesare from her life, leaving her to seize her happiness with both hands.

When he spoke again, Perry's voice was grave.

'You must be honest with me,' he said quietly. 'Have you still some reservations? You misjudge your father. He would not have offered you in marriage unless he believed that it would mean your happiness.'

'It isn't only that!' she murmured. 'Won't you give me time? I had not expected…I didn't think you loved me.'

'Can you doubt it?' Gently Perry removed her from his lap. Then he rose to his feet. 'Your aunt was right. I should have taken her advice and waited. You don't yet trust in the strength of my affection.'

He waited, hoping for a denial, but Elizabeth did not speak.

'Shall we go?' he said. With extreme formality he bowed and led her from the room.

Elizabeth's misery knew no bounds. It needed no words of his to tell her that she had wounded him to the heart. She could only guess at the depths of his disappointment. It was no deeper than her own. She could not have suffered more if a knife had been thrust into her breast.

She longed to run away, to escape from the cruel fates which seemed determined to pursue her, yet all about her the merriment continued. In disbelief she heard the chimes of a long-case clock. It was still too early to plead exhaustion and beg to be taken home.

Besides, the Prince of Wales was due at any moment. Miss Grantham would not commit the social gaffe of leaving before his arrival.

'There you are, my dear.' Miss Grantham was engaged in conversation with the Earl of Brandon. 'We were beginning to think that you had vanished. Now here is yet another partner come to claim you...' She nodded pleasantly to a young man who was waiting at some little distance, and turned back to the Earl.

Had she noticed nothing amiss? Elizabeth could not believe it. In these last few hours her world had been turned to dust and ashes. Forcing a mechanical smile, she allowed herself to be led out to join in the quadrille.

Meantime, Perry leaned against a pillar, scanning the crowded room.

'Looking for someone, old chap?'

Perry turned to find Lord Christopher beside him.

'Count Cesare di Tavola. Have you seen him?'

'Can't say that I know him, but the name sounds familiar. Ain't he Elizabeth's friend?'

'That I take leave to doubt. Didn't you see him dancing with her?' There was a note in Perry's voice which filled Chris with alarm.

'You mean that capering creature with the rainbow waistcoat? Hard to miss him, really. He looks like a popinjay with all those frills and fobs. Can't be him, though. Ain't he still in Italy?'

'He's here!' Perry said briefly. 'Chris, will you act for me?'

'Pleasure, old chap, as long as Elizabeth is not involved! Can't have a lady's name brought into this. The story would be all round London.'

'Elizabeth will not be mentioned. I believe that I have taken exception to his waistcoat.'

'You will when you see it, but you can't fight him, Perry. The fellow ain't a gentleman. He may call himself a Count, but he looks like a mountebank to me. Besides, he lives in a tree. Dashed bad *ton*, I call it!'

If Chris had hoped that his attempt at humour would raise a smile, he was mistaken. Perry's face grew even darker.

'He won't avoid a thrashing!'

'Same thing applies. In these past few days you've squired Elizabeth about. Dash it, man, you can't thrash him because he danced with her. You know what the world will say.'

'Suppose I tell you that she has suffered violence at his hands? Her wrist still bears the marks. Stand aside! I think I see him.'

'Wait!' Chris laid a hand upon his arm. 'Do you tell me that he was trying to coerce her?' He sounded deeply shocked.

Perry disengaged himself. 'He shall answer to me for that!'

'Not here! Let's take a turn about the terrace. I fancy blowing a cloud.'

'At a time like this?' Perry sneered.

'Especially at a time like this. There's something devilish smoky here. Did you ask her why he tried to force her?'

Perry shook his head. 'She was too distraught. I tried to comfort her, and much good it did me.' His face was a mask of anguish.

Chris took his arm and drew him out on to the terrace.

'Think, man, think! Don't it strike you as odd? Elizabeth is no milk-and-water miss. Something must have frightened her.'

Perry stared at him. 'Perhaps he tried to kiss her. They were once betrothed.'

'You ain't thinking straight. Why would she struggle if she still loves him?'

'I don't know.' Perry leaned against the stone balustrade. His thoughts were in turmoil.

'She don't, you know. It's you she wants. Are you blind? You and she have been smelling of April and May for long enough.'

'I'm not so sure. She won't agree to marry me.'

'You've asked her again?'

'I did, and she refused. I should be used to it by now, but it doesn't get any easier.'

'There must be some reason. Sounds to me as if she had an argument with this so-called Count, and a violent one at that. He may have come for her, and been rejected. Cheer up, old lad! He ain't in any position to force her into marriage, unless...' The implications of what he'd been about to say caused the words to die upon his lips.

'Were you about to tell me that he might have some hold upon her?'

'Don't jump to conclusions!' Chris backed away before the look on Perry's face. 'We know nothing yet, but we could find out.'

'How? I won't confront Elizabeth with such a slur upon her character.'

'I didn't mean anything like that. I was thinking that we might get the fellow to damn himself out of his own mouth.'

'Unlikely! He's a cunning devil.'

'But suppose we set a trap? If we could lure him into another interview with Elizabeth?'

'Out of the question! I won't expose her to further violence.'

'She'd be in no danger if you were in the room...say, behind a screen?'

'I don't like it. It's an underhand way of going on.'

Chris summoned all his courage. 'Afraid of what you might hear?' he asked.

He had expected an explosion of wrath, but to his astonishment, Perry smiled.

'I love her, Chris,' he answered quietly. 'Nothing Elizabeth could say or do will alter that, but I have no fears. She is as honest as the day.'

'Then you agree? Think quickly! Is there some anteroom where you might be undisturbed?'

Perry walked further along the terrace and entered the study by the long French windows. 'In here, I think. How are we to go about it?'

Chris looked about the room. 'This screen will serve, if you crouch down. I'll move this lamp closer to the door, so that you are in shadow. Keep quiet, and leave the rest to me...'

## Chapter Fourteen

As Chris re-entered the ballroom, the music suddenly died away. A hush descended on the crowd, and then he heard the sound of clapping.

Looking up, he saw the figure of the Prince of Wales, making his way down the centre of the room with the Earl of Brandon by his side.

At any other time Chris might have shown more interest in the heir to the throne, but he did not spare a second glance for the fair-haired man who smiled so graciously upon his fellow guests.

He made his way to Elizabeth's side. Her pallor was alarming, and caused her aunt to whisper to her before the royal party reached them.

'My dear, the Prince will not eat you. His charm is legendary.' Clearly she ascribed her niece's ashen look to a mixture of shyness and excitement.

Chris gripped Elizabeth's elbow. 'Hold on!' he murmured. 'There is no need for you to worry. All will be well, I promise.'

He doubted if she had understood his words of reassurance. She was swaying on her feet.

'Perry tells me that you didn't get your lemonade,' he continued. 'When this is over, you shall sit quietly and I will fetch you a drink.'

She gave him a look of gratitude, but he didn't see it. He was scanning the room for his quarry.

Pray heaven that the Count had not already left. No, there he was, pushing to the forefront of the crowd and smirking in anticipation.

The fellow hopes to be presented, Chris thought indignantly. If so, he had reckoned without the Earl of Brandon. That gentleman looked through him as he and the Prince drew level. It was a studied insult, and the Count's face darkened.

Would he leave in anger? Chris could not contain his impatience as the royal guest moved on. Must he chat to everyone for so long?

When he reached them at last, Chris made his bow. Then he stood aside as Miss Grantham and her niece were presented.

Elizabeth was surprised to find that Prince George and her aunt stood upon such easy terms. She sank to the floor in a deep curtsy, blushing at his compliments.

'You've been hiding this jewel, Mary,' the Prince was pleased to say. 'I shall take you to task for that.'

'Your Royal Highness is very kind.' Miss Grantham was unabashed. She had known the young man since he was a child. She liked him, appreciating his patronage of the arts, whilst deploring his extravagance and his constant feuding with his father.

When the Prince moved away, Chris spoke out. 'May I take Elizabeth to supper, ma'am? She must be parched and hungry...'

'She does look pale,' Miss Grantham agreed. 'Go

with Lord Christopher, my dear. Some refreshment will restore you.'

Elizabeth allowed herself to be led away. She felt that she was moving in a trance. This was some dreadful dream from which she must awaken.

'Not the dining-room,' she whispered. 'I could not eat...the food would choke me.'

'Shall you care to walk out on the terrace?' he suggested. 'It will be cooler there, and further along there is a quiet room. You could rest for a time, and I will fetch your lemonade.'

She made no protest, nor did she speak again, and his suspicions grew. Something was sadly wrong here. Were he and Perry right to subject her to another ordeal?

At that moment he could have strangled the Count with his bare hands, but there was no time to lose. Even now, the fellow might be calling for his carriage.

Once in the study he glanced towards the screen, noting with satisfaction that it was obscured by shadows. There was neither sight nor sound of Perry. With what seemed to him to be ungallant haste he excused himself, but Elizabeth did not notice. She sat in the wing-chair, gazing into space.

So far, so good! Now he must find the Count. To his dismay, the fellow seemed to have vanished. Then his eye fell upon his quarry. The man was taking part in a quadrille.

Chris was blessed with an equable temperament, but now his anger knew no bounds. The fellow would soon be dancing to a different tune, he thought with satisfaction.

As the dance ended he touched the Count upon the shoulder.

'Sir, I am charged with a message for you from Miss Elizabeth Grantham. She begs that you will wait upon her in the study.'

An arch smile greeted his words. 'These ladies, my dear sir! So mysterious! What are we to do with them?'

Chris was sorely tempted to plant him a facer. The fellow was actually preening himself. Instead he nodded. 'You know the way?'

'No. I shall be obliged if you will show me.'

'A pleasure, sir.' This was true, although Chris did not specify exactly in what his pleasure lay.

His companion took the words for the well-known courtesy of an English gentleman.

When they reached the study, Chris threw open the door and motioned to the Count to enter. He would have given much to be behind the screen with Perry, but he could only wait. He had carried out his own part in the plan to expose this insufferable creature.

As it was, he heard only the Count's first words to Elizabeth.

'Well, my dear? Are you come to your senses at last?'

Startled, Elizabeth gazed at him in horror.

'Has the cat got your tongue?' he demanded. 'Since you sent for me, I am come for your decision.'

'Sent for you?' she whispered. 'I did not send for you.'

'Odd! Some fellow told me that you wished to see me.' He was too sure of his power over her for

the least suspicion to cross his mind. 'It is no matter.
He must have seen us dancing together and decided
to play Cupid. The English, I find, have a perverted
sense of humour.'

'I have nothing to say to you,' she cried in desperation. 'Please go away!'

'Still clinging to the hope that I won't carry out
my threats, my love? What an innocent you are!
You may rid yourself of that idea. A word from me,
dropped in the right circles, and you will never lift
your head again.'

'But it is lies! All lies! You were never admitted
to my bedchamber. All that ever passed between us
was romantic nonsense. You sent me flowers...you
kissed my hand...but that was all.'

'I know that, and so do you, but will the world
believe it? What a little fool you were! Have you
not learned that you must not play with fire?'

'I've learned how contemptible you are. You disgust me!' Elizabeth's chin went up. 'Don't think that
you can frighten me, you...you spy!'

The Count had taken a step towards her, but he
stopped. 'Dear me!' he murmured softly. 'You are
a greater danger than I thought. Where did you hear
such rumours?' His voice was silky with menace.

'They aren't rumours. They are the truth. Where
did you get the money for your clothing and your
jewels?'

'One makes shift where one can, my dear. How
can I keep you in the manner to which you are accustomed without a handsome fortune...in addition
to your own, I mean?'

'Then you don't deny it?'

'Within these four walls? No! It would be pointless, but it cannot signify. You have no proof, and even if you had, a wife cannot testify against her husband.'

'I shall never be your wife. You may spread your evil calumnies. To be disgraced is preferable to being married to a monster of depravity.'

'Brave words, my dear, but they won't save you.' He came towards her then, and she put out a hand to fend him off.

'Take care!' she cried. 'Your activities are known to others—'

'Really?' He seized her arm and twisted it behind her back. 'Give me their names.'

A gasp of pain escaped Elizabeth's lips. Then, before she could reply, the searing agony stopped.

To her astonishment the Count was lifted high, and shaken as a terrier might shake a rat.

Dreadful choking sounds issued from his lips, and his face grew purple.

Elizabeth looked at the bulging eyes, and then she grabbed at Perry's arm.

'Stop!' she cried. 'You'll kill him. My darling, he isn't worth it!'

For a moment she thought he hadn't heard her. This was a man she didn't know. Perry was beyond all reason, and there was murder in his expression.

'Leave him!' she urged again. 'He won't escape the law! Will you have his blood upon your hands?'

The red light faded from Perry's eyes. Then he threw the limp figure from him.

'I should break his neck! Did he injure you, my love?'

'No, no!' Elizabeth seized his hand and held it to her cheek. He kissed it briefly, and moved her aside.

The Count had struggled to his hands and knees, but he did not dare to rise.

'Get up, you cur! Would you attack a woman? Try me instead! I'll teach you a lesson you won't forget!'

Desperate for some way of escape, Cesare glanced about the study, but the door was closed, and Perry stood between himself and the open window.

'Get up, I say, or must I kick you from this room?'

'Strong words, Perry!' The Earl of Brandon strolled in from the terrace. 'What is this person doing upon his hands and knees? Am I disturbing some unusual amusement?' He picked up the lamp and advanced into the room.

'This is a trap!' Cesare found his voice at last. 'I might have known it! You English! You think you are so clever!'

An ominous silence greeted his words. He rose to his feet, and loosened the cravat which had come so close to strangling him.

'You haven't heard the last of this,' he threatened. 'I am an Italian national. When my Ambassador learns that I was offered violence here tonight, it will cause a diplomatic incident!'

'Violence, my dear sir? Were there witnesses?' The Earl smiled upon his guest. 'I thought you merely searching for that rather splendid ruby tie-pin which now seems to have disappeared...'

'Very clever, my noble lord, but you won't save your brother. He was about to kill me!'

'Extraordinary! And for no reason, sir? You must

take more care of your person. Such a pity that
London is become so dangerous!'

The Count's face grew dark with rage. 'Would
you threaten me? You and your family will regret
it.'

'Do you think so? We can scarce be held responsible for those cutthroats who lurk about the streets
at night, or the actions of a press-gang...'

'You would not dare!' A muscle began to twitch
beside Cesare's mouth, and his face grew pale with
terror. He looked at the Earl of Brandon's face, but
he saw no mercy there.

'Our guest might enjoy a sea-trip,' Perry suggested smoothly. 'After all, he is so interested in the
movements of our shipping. A voyage would be just
the thing for him.'

The Count backed slowly towards the door, a pis-
tol appearing in his hand. It was levelled at
Elizabeth's heart.

'Stand back!' he ordered. 'If you value her life,
you won't try to rush me.'

'My dear sir, I shouldn't dream of it.' The Earl
brushed an imaginary speck of dirt from his coat,
and the gesture was not lost on Cesare.

'Arrogant devils!' he shouted. 'You English think
you own the world. I'll see you all in hell before
I've done.' He reached behind him for the door-
knob, his eyes still fixed on his tormentors.

'A candidate for Bedlam, I believe. Don't you
think so, Perry. I wonder if anyone will listen to his
ravings.'

'Not a hope of it! Clearly his mind is over-set.'
If he could keep the fellow talking, Perry hoped to
move his own body to shield Elizabeth. She was still

in Cesare's line of fire. He stepped towards her slowly.

'Don't move, or I'll kill her where she stands!' Cesare's finger tightened on the trigger, and Perry froze, cursing inwardly.

He should never have exposed her to such danger. Better by far to allow his quarry to escape him. The man might yet kill her in revenge.

Then the door opened and Cesare backed away. He did not see the men behind him, and as he turned to flee his arms were seized by two burly individuals in the red coats of the Bow Street Runners.

Cesare twisted away from them. With a cry he rushed across the room towards the open window, but Perry was too quick for him. He stepped forward, raised his arm, and sent his enemy crashing to the ground.

The Earl stepped forward and looked at the inert figure.

'Perry, that upper-cut was lacking in technique,' he murmured. 'You must spend more time in training.' He raised a finger, and the Bow Street men came forward. 'My guest is leaving. May I rely on you to help him on his way? You had best go by the terrace.'

The two men grinned. Both were ex-pugilists, and the Earl was known to be a keen supporter of the Fancy.

They eyed him with respect. 'Back to Bow Street, my lord?'

'Yes. Your superior officer has arranged a reception committee, I believe. Take him away.' Brandon strolled over to the bell-pull.

'Briggs, I believe we should like some wine,' he

told his butler. 'Have you any preference, Miss Grantham?'

Elizabeth shook her head. She was clutching Perry's hand, and his arm was about her waist.

The Earl's eyes twinkled. 'Then it shall be champagne. Always suitable for a celebration.'

'We have much to celebrate.' Perry's face was radiant. 'Frederick, won't you wish us happy?'

'With all my heart, my dear fellow. Miss Grantham, do you know what you are taking on? This great brother of mine is a sad rogue...'

Elizabeth dimpled. 'He has told me your opinion of him, sir. Did you not say that he had a deplorable tendency to levity?'

'It's perfectly true, my dear. That is but one of his faults. The others you will discover for yourself.' His smiling eyes belied the truth of his words.

'I didn't feel much like laughing tonight,' Perry admitted. 'What will you do with him?'

'The matter is now out of my hands, but I think you need not fear to see the Count again. Shall we leave it at that?' He raised his glass to the happy couple.

His manner was urbane, but Elizabeth was under no illusions. This was a dangerous man. In the face of his power, Cesare's threats and posturings were no more than the babblings of a child.

'You must excuse me,' the Earl continued. 'The Prince was fully occupied when I left him, but I mustn't neglect my duties as host.' He took Elizabeth's hand and pressed it warmly. 'Welcome to our family, my dear.' With that, he left the room, closing the door behind him.

Perry took Elizabeth in his arms. 'Kiss me, my love,' he murmured.

She lifted up her face to his, gazing deep into his eyes. Then his mouth came down on hers, and she was swept away on a dizzying tide of passion.

Perry released her at last, leaving her breathless.

'Tell me now,' he urged. 'When shall we be wed? I want you so, my darling. Will you keep me waiting?'

'It shall be whenever you wish,' she told him simply. 'Oh, Perry, I love you dearly, but we must tell Aunt Mary. She will be surprised.'

This brought a shout of laughter from her love. 'You think she has not guessed? She knew that you loved me before I did myself.'

'Oh!' Elizabeth coloured. 'I thought I hid my feelings very well.'

'Too well, on occasion. Why did you not tell me of the Count's attempt at blackmail?'

'I was afraid,' she said in a low voice. 'I thought you might believe him, and I could not bear to have you think so ill of me.'

'As if I should! What a little goose you are! Would I take the word of a cur like that against your own?'

'I did tell you that he was my betrothed,' she protested.

'You told me many things, and I didn't believe one half of them. Now I must be convinced that you wish to become my bride.' Smiling, he bent his head to kiss her again.

'I long for nothing more!' Elizabeth threw her arms about his neck, but a last lingering doubt remained. 'What will happen to Cesare? He threatened to cause a scandal, and we must think of your family, and Aunt Mary.'

Perry sat down and took her on his lap. 'Forget him!' he advised. 'Frederick is not given to making idle promises. You may take his word that you have nothing more to fear.'

Elizabeth swallowed. 'He would not...I mean... neither of you would take his life?'

'Great heavens, my dear! Murder is forbidden in this country. We are not barbarians, as you once believed.'

She smiled at the reference to her angry accusations. 'I've changed my mind,' she said. 'Of course, because of his spying, Cesare does not deserve to live, but I could not bear it if you or your brother were to be taken up for killing him.'

'My lordly relative a common criminal? Perish the thought! Frederick told us, did he not, that the matter is out of his hands? The Count will be asked to leave the country...that is all.'

His words seemed to satisfy her, but for his own part, Perry suspected that the Count was unlikely to enjoy a long life. For all his charm, Frederick could be ruthless where the interests of his country were concerned. With a shrug he dismissed any further conjecture as to the Count's fate. The fellow was not worth a second thought.

Perry held Elizabeth close. His lips were against her hair.

'What a merry dance you led me!' he said fondly. 'I suspected that it would be so from the moment I first saw you.'

'Did you?' She kissed the hollow of his neck. 'It was the same with me. I hated you, you know.'

'You made that clear, my darling. What caused you to change your mind?'

'I can't imagine!' she told him wickedly. 'I must be losing my mind.'

'I lost mine long ago, together with my heart.' He silenced her with a lingering kiss, sure now that he had won his bride.

\* \* \* \* \*

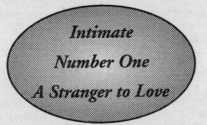

# *Historical Romance*™

## *Coming next month*

### REBECCA'S ROGUE
### by Paula Marshall

*A Regency delight!*

Will was the perfect candidate—desperate
enough to marry Rebecca for her money and
agree to her conditions, but handsome enough
that it was easy to convince society that they had
married for love—almost *too* easy!

### DEAR DECEIVER
### by Mary Nichols

*A Regency delight!*

Who was Emma Woodhill? And why did
Dominic care especially when he was sure that
Emma was lying to him and he was engaged to
marry someone else? But he *did* care—fiancée or
no fiancée.

## On sale from 13th July 1998

# COLLECTOR'S EDITION

The *Penny Jordan Collector's Edition* is
a selection of her most popular stories,
published in beautifully designed volumes
for you to collect and cherish.

*Available from Tesco, Asda, WH Smith, John Menzies,*
*Martins and all good paperback stockists, at £3.10 each -*
*or the special price of £2.80 if you use the coupon below.*
*On sale from 1st June 1998.*

Valid only in the UK & Eire against purchases made in retail outlets and not in
conjunction with any Reader Service or other offer.

---

# 30ᵖ OFF
## COUPON
VALID UNTIL: 31.8.1998

### PENNY JORDAN COLLECTOR'S EDITION

**To the Customer:** This coupon can be used in part payment for a
copy of PENNY JORDAN COLLECTOR'S EDITION. Only one
coupon can be used against each copy purchased. Valid only in the
UK & Eire against purchases made in retail outlets and not in
conjunction with any Reader Service or other offer. Please do not
attempt to redeem this coupon against any other product as refusal
to accept may cause embarrassment and delay at the checkout.

**To the Retailer:** Harlequin Mills & Boon will redeem this coupon at
face value provided only that it has been taken in part payment for
any book in the PENNY JORDAN COLLECTOR'S EDITION. The
company reserves the right to refuse payment against misredeemed
coupons. Please submit coupons to: Harlequin Mills & Boon Ltd.
NCH Dept 730, Corby, Northants NN17 1NN.

9 904170 250306

0472 01316